BASIC SKILLS WITH MATH

NEW REVISED

BASIC SKILLS WITH MATH

Whole Numbers

JERRY HOWETT

CAMBRIDGE ADULT EDUCATION

EDITORIAL DEVELOPER: Cathy Fillmore Hoyt

EDITORS: Stephanie Cahill, Doug Falk, Dena Pollak, Phyllis Dunsay

PRODUCTION EDITOR: Alan Dalgleish, Suzanne Keezer

BOOK DESIGN: Parallelogram, New York

ELECTRONIC PAGE PRODUCTION: Burmar Technical Corporation, Albertson, New York

COVER ART: Salem Krieger

COVER DESIGN: Patricia Battipede

ISBN 0-835-95736-5
Printed in the United States of America
4 5 6 7 8   08 07 06 05 04

PEARSON
Learning
Group

1-800-321-3106
www.pearsonlearning.com

▽ **Contents**

Unit 5. Division

— WHOLE NUMBERS PREVIEW —

The first step in building math skill is finding out what you need to work on. To help you find out, work the problems beginning on this page. Do all the problems you can. Do not use a calculator. Don't worry about problems you're not sure you know how to work. This book will help you learn how to work the problems you missed or did not do. Check your answers and fill in the chart on page 5. The right-hand side of the chart lists the pages you need to work on.

In problems 1 to 4, read the number. Then write out the missing words in the name of the number.

1. 82,306   eighty-two _____ , three hundred six

2. 2,596,480   two _____, five hundred ninety-six

   _____, four hundred eighty

3. 6,083,700   six _____, eighty-three _____ ,

   seven _____

4. 1,280,500,000   one _____ , two hundred

   eighty _____ ,

   five hundred _____

In problems 5 to 8, read the numbers. Then write the numbers in figures.

5. nine hundred six   _____

6. four hundred twenty thousand, three hundred   _____

7. two million, three hundred five thousand   _____

8. eighteen million, fifty-six thousand, nine hundred   _____

9. Round 564 to the nearest ten.   _____

10. Round 12,973 to the nearest hundred.   _____

11.   431
    + 258

12.   6,027
    + 3,951

13.   720,463
    + 258,134

14. 807 + 92 =

15. 26 + 432 =

16. 92,134 + 6,523 =

17.   83
      97
    + 46

18.   237
      72
    + 894

19.   3,407
     19,589
    + 6,374

20.   6,882
      1,924
    + 3,297

21.   23,206
      14,583
    + 27,375

22.   186,407
      29,336
    + 152,593

23. 85 + 1,263 + 171 =

24. 3,075 + 288 + 16 =

25. An empty ship weighs 10,245 tons. It carries boxes that weigh a total of 8,948 tons. Find the combined weight of the ship and the boxes.

26.   93
    − 22

27.   756
    − 124

28.   49,186
    − 28,072

29. 6,894 − 2,713 =

30. $\begin{array}{r} 74 \\ -28 \\ \hline \end{array}$
31. $\begin{array}{r} 6,227 \\ -2,598 \\ \hline \end{array}$
32. $\begin{array}{r} 83,106 \\ -24,872 \\ \hline \end{array}$
33. $\begin{array}{r} 826,453 \\ -96,875 \\ \hline \end{array}$

34. $6,251 - 3,487 =$

35. $29,216 - 19,538 =$

36. $\begin{array}{r} 300 \\ -148 \\ \hline \end{array}$
37. $\begin{array}{r} 7,000 \\ -1,234 \\ \hline \end{array}$
38. $\begin{array}{r} 30,500 \\ -19,386 \\ \hline \end{array}$
39. $2,000 - 1,573 =$

40. Al bought a pair of boots for $65. How much change did he get from $80?

41. $\begin{array}{r} 843 \\ \times \quad 2 \\ \hline \end{array}$
42. $\begin{array}{r} 63 \\ \times 21 \\ \hline \end{array}$
43. $\begin{array}{r} 413 \\ \times 223 \\ \hline \end{array}$
44. $\begin{array}{r} 3,042 \\ \times \quad 221 \\ \hline \end{array}$

45. $\begin{array}{r} 94 \\ \times 6 \\ \hline \end{array}$
46. $\begin{array}{r} 780 \\ \times \quad 6 \\ \hline \end{array}$
47. $\begin{array}{r} 57 \\ \times 63 \\ \hline \end{array}$
48. $\begin{array}{r} 852 \\ \times 60 \\ \hline \end{array}$

49. $\begin{array}{r} 847 \\ \times 36 \\ \hline \end{array}$
50. $\begin{array}{r} 2,934 \\ \times \quad 85 \\ \hline \end{array}$
51. $9 \times 817 =$

52. $526 \times 49 =$

53. $83 \times 197 =$

54. $6,093 \times 412 =$

55. $10 \times 2,500 =$

56. $1,000 \times 28 =$

57. Jane earns $8 an hour. How much does she earn for 38 hours of work?

58. $7\overline{)322}$ **59.** $5\overline{)3,520}$ **60.** $8\overline{)2,288}$ **61.** $6\overline{)148}$

62. $9\overline{)5,521}$ **63.** $32\overline{)256}$ **64.** $18\overline{)738}$ **65.** $91\overline{)3,923}$

66. $23\overline{)1,857}$ **67.** $42\overline{)1,139}$ **68.** $218\overline{)13,516}$ **69.** $479\overline{)16,286}$

70. $1,890 \div 42 =$ **71.** $702 \div 18 =$ **72.** $1,992 \div 83 =$

73. 480 people bought tickets to a custom car show. There were 427 people who actually went. How many of the people who bought tickets did not go?

74. Jack is buying supplies. He estimates he will spend $15 for paint, $4 for a brush, $5 for paint thinner, and $2 for sales tax. Find the total of his estimates.

75. An airplane flies at an average speed of 394 miles per hour. How far can the plane travel in seven hours? [**Hint:** Multiply the number of hours the plane travels by the speed per hour.]

76. One ton contains 2,000 pounds. How many tons are there in 846,000 pounds?

77. David is a salesman. In the last 10 days he sold $1,290 worth of shoes. What was the average amount that he sold each day? [**Hint:** Divide the total sales by the number of days to find the average sold per day.]

78. Mark paid $165 every month for 36 months to pay off a loan. What was the total amount that he paid?

Check your answers on page 105. Then complete the chart below.

Problem numbers	Number of problems in this section	Number of problems you got right in this section	
1 to 10	10	_____	If you had fewer than 8 problems right, go to page 6.
11 to 25, and 74	16	_____	If you had fewer than 13 problems right, go to page 19.
26 to 40, and 73	16	_____	If you had fewer than 13 problems right, go to page 35.
41 to 57, 75 and 78	19	_____	If you had fewer than 15 problems right, go to page 54.
58 to 72, 76, and 77	17	_____	If you had fewer than 14 problems right, go to page 77.

Beginning Whole Numbers

Place Value in Whole Numbers

Whole numbers are made up of the **digits** 0, 1, 2, 3, 4, 5, 6, 7, 8, and 9. The number 33 has two digits. The number 40,280 has five digits. The value of each digit is different because of its position in the number. Every position has a **place value.** The table below gives the names of the first ten places in our whole number system.

_____ , _____ _____ _____ , _____ _____ _____ , _____ _____ _____

billions, hundred millions, ten millions, millions, hundred thousands, ten thousands, thousands, hundreds, tens, units or ones

The first 3 in the number 33 is in the tens place. It has a value of 3 tens or 30. The second 3 is in the units or ones place. It has a value of 3 ones or 3. The digit is still 3, but the value is different because of the digit's place.

The 4 in the number 40,280 is in the ten thousands place. It has a value of 4 ten thousands or 40,000. The 2 is in the hundreds place. It has a value of 2 hundreds or 200. The 8 is in the tens place. It has a value of 8 tens or 80.

Notice that the value of the thousands position and the value of the units position in the number 40,280 are both 0. The 0 holds the place so the other digits can be written in the right place.

Example: Find the value of 6 in 26,354.

The 6 is in the thousands place. It has a value of 6 thousands or 6,000.

PRACTICE I

Solve.

1. Underline the two-digit numbers.

   265   86   9   5,923   13   99   450

2. Underline the three-digit numbers.

   800   33   6,920   15   204   871   1,495

3. Underline the four-digit numbers.

   1,998   342   40,000   5,690   18,050   16

4. Underline the digit in the ones place in each number.

   87   230   7,229   6   392   24,781

5. Underline the digit in the tens place in each number.

   87   230   7,229   506   392   24,781

6. Underline the digit in the hundreds place in each number.

   487   230   7,229   506   392   24,781

7. Underline the digit in the thousands place in each number.

39,200 6,230 7,229 781,000 3,278,500

Use the number 416 to answer questions 8 to 10. Item 8 is done for you.

8. 4 is in the ___*hundreds*___ place. 4 has a value of ___*400*___.

9. 1 is in the _____ place. 1 has a value of _____.

10. 6 is in the _____ place. 6 has a value of _____.

Use the number 79,300 to answer questions 11 to 13.

11. 7 is in the _____ place. 7 has a value of _____.

12. 9 is in the _____ place. 9 has a value of _____.

13. 3 is in the _____ place. 3 has a value of _____.

There are 5,280 feet in a mile. Use this number to answer questions 14 to 16.

14. 5 is in the _____ place. 5 has a value of _____.

15. 2 is in the _____ place. 2 has a value of _____.

16. In 1990 the population of the metropolitan area of Cheyenne was 73,142. What is the value of 7 in this number?

To check your answers, turn to page 105.

Reading Whole Numbers

Commas make numbers easier to read. Counting from the right, there is a comma after every three places. Large numbers are read in these same groups of three. At each comma we say the name of the group of digits that are set off by the comma.

Examples: 2,560 = two thousand, five hundred sixty

85,409 = eighty-five thousand, four hundred nine

3,280,000 = three million, two hundred eighty thousand

Notice how the commas go in the same place whether the number is written in words or figures.

PRACTICE 2

For problems 1 to 3, choose the word form for each number.

1. 6,700
   a. six hundred seventy
   b. six thousand, seven hundred
   c. sixty thousand, seven
   d. six hundred seven

2. 14,090
   a. fourteen thousand, ninety
   b. fourteen thousand, nine hundred
   c. one hundred forty-nine thousand
   d. fourteen thousand, nine

3. 208,000
   a. two hundred eighty thousand
   b. two hundred thousand, eight hundred
   c. two hundred thousand, eight
   d. two hundred eight thousand

For problems 4 to 12, supply the missing words you need to read each number.

4. 29,450

   twenty-nine _____ , four hundred fifty

5. 163,208

   one hundred sixty-three _____ , two hundred eight

6. 30,407,380

   thirty _____, four hundred seven _____ ,

   three hundred eighty

7. 903

   nine _____ three

8. 8,017,600

   eight _____ , seventeen _____ , six _____

9. 2,600

   two _____ , six _____

10. 2,006

    two _____ , six

11. 875,400

    eight hundred seventy-five _____,

    four _____

12. 6,005,890

six ______________ , five ______________ ,

eight hundred ninety

Write words to show how to read each number.

13. 3,490 ____

14. 82,650 ____

15. 3,009,025 ____

To check your answers, turn to page 106.

Writing Whole Numbers

Every month Marta writes a check for five hundred nine dollars to pay rent.

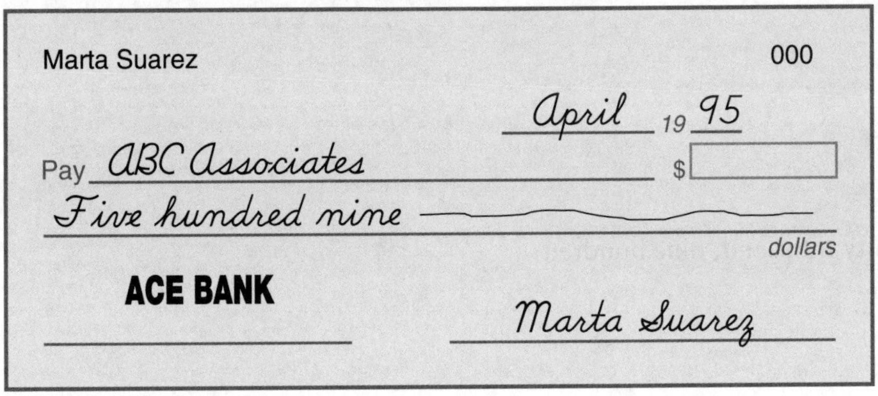

To write numbers from words, watch for places that must be held with zeros.

Example: Write five hundred nine.

This number has no tens. Hold the tens place with a zero. 509

➡ Marta's check is for $509.

Example: Write four hundred thousand, eight hundred seven.

This number has no ten thousands, no thousands, and no tens. Hold these places with zeros.

400,807

Example: Write twenty thousand, sixty.

This number has no thousands, no hundreds, and no units. Hold these places with zeros.

20,060

PRACTICE 3

For problems 1 to 5, choose the correctly written form for each number.

1. seven thousand, three hundred
   a. 73,000
   b. 7,003
   c. 7,030
   d. 7,300

2. three hundred twenty-five thousand
   a. 3,250
   b. 32,500
   c. 325,000
   d. 3,250,000

3. one million, six hundred eighty thousand, nine hundred
   a. 1,680,900
   b. 1,600,890
   c. 1,608,900
   d. 1,068,900

4. In 1993 the average daily circulation of *USA Today* was one million, four hundred ninety-five thousand.
   a. 1,000,495
   b. 1,400,095
   c. 1,495,000
   d. 1,490,005

5. The average distance from Earth to the sun is ninety-two million, nine hundred sixty thousand miles.
   a.   9,296,000
   b.   92,960,000
   c.   92,096,000
   d. 926,960,000

Use the digits 0, 1, 2, 3, 4, 5, 6, 7, 8, and 9 to write each of the following.

6. five hundred seven   _____

7. two hundred sixty-five thousand   _____

8. eighteen thousand, four hundred   _____

9. thirty thousand, eight hundred seventy   _____

10. four million, eight thousand, two hundred   _____

11. six hundred twenty thousand, three hundred four _____

12. eighty thousand, sixty-five   _____

13. forty thousand, nine hundred twenty   _____

14. one million, two hundred eighty thousand   _____

15. two thousand, ninety   _____

16. sixty thousand, five hundred   _____   *To check your answers, turn to page 106.*

Rounding Whole Numbers

Marla's pickup truck weighs 3,862 pounds. What is the weight of her truck to the nearest 100 pounds?

To find the weight of the truck to the nearest 100 pounds, you must **round off** 3,862. Rounding makes numbers easier to use when you don't need exact values. To round off a number, you must know the place value of each digit in the number.

To round a whole number:

1. Underline the digit in the place to which you want to round.

2. If the digit to the right of the underlined digit is more than 4, add 1 to the underlined digit.

3. If the digit to the right of the underlined digit is less than 5, do not change the underlined digit.

4. Replace the digits to the right of the underlined digit with zeros.

Example: Round 3,862 to the nearest hundred.

STEP 1.   Underline the digit in the hundreds   3,8̲62
           place, 8.

STEP 2.   The digit to the right of 8 is 6. Add 1   3,900
           to 8, and replace 6 and 2 with zeros.

➠   To the nearest 100 pounds, Marla's truck weighs 3,900 pounds.

Example: Round 2,713 to the nearest ten.

STEP 1.   Underline the digit in the tens   2,71̲3
           place, 1.

STEP 2.   The digit to the right of 1 is 3. Do   2,710
           not change 1, but replace 3 with
           a zero.

Example: Round 19,732 to the nearest thousand.

STEP 1.   Underline the digit in the thousands   19,732
           place, 9.

STEP 2.   The digit to the right of 9 is 7. Add   20,000
           1 to 9. Since 1 + 9 = 10, you must
           carry 1 over to the ten-thousands
           column. Replace 7, 3, and 2 with
           zeros.

PRACTICE 4

Solve.

1. Round each number to the nearest ten.

   26   283   5,017   698   1,474

2. Round each number to the nearest hundred.

   639   26,451   8,076   4,977   385,130

3. Round each number to the nearest thousand.

   18,620   7,288   413,728   9,800   66,295

4. Round each number to the nearest ten thousand.

   18,620   7,288   413,728   159,000   66,295

5. Round each number to the nearest hundred thousand.

   129,999   3,615,277   40,291,330   155,400   8,965,000

6. Round each number to the nearest million.

2,385,000   12,850,000   4,720,800   9,860,000   32,170,000

Use the following information to answer questions 7 to 9.

The Concerned Parents League has raised $2,867 for new playground equipment.

7. Find the amount to the nearest $10.   _____

8. Find the amount to the nearest $100.   _____

9. Find the amount to the nearest $1000.   _____

Use the following information to answer questions 10 to 12.

In 1990 the population of Harris County, Texas, was 2,818,199.

10. Find the population to the nearest ten thousand.   _____

11. Find the population to the nearest hundred thousand.   _____

12. Find the population to the nearest million.   _____   *To check your answers, turn to page 107.*

BEGINNING WHOLE NUMBERS REVIEW

The problems on this page will help you find out if you need to review the beginning section of this book. When you finish, look at the chart to see which pages you should review.

Use the number 85,260 to answer questions 1 to 3.

1. Which digit is in the tens place? _____

2. Which digit is in the thousands place? _____

3. The digit 2 is in the _____ place.

Supply the missing words needed to read the numbers in problems 4 and 5.

4. 15,630 fifteen _____, six _____ thirty

5. 9,040,800 nine _____ , forty _____ ,

   eight _____

Use the digits 0 to 9 to write the numbers in problems 6 to 8.

6. seven thousand eighty _____

7. two hundred three thousand, fifteen _____

8. three million, twenty-seven thousand, four hundred _____

Use the number 14,972 to solve problems 9 to 11.

9. Round the number to the nearest ten. _____

10. Round the number to the nearest hundred. _____

11. Round the number to the nearest thousand. _____

PROGRESS CHECK

Check your answers on page 107. Then return to the review pages for the problems you missed. Correct your answers before going on to the next unit.

If you missed problems	Review pages
1, 2, or 3	6 to 8
4 or 5	9 to 10
6, 7, or 8	11 to 13
9, 10, or 11	14 to 16

Addition

Addition Facts

You can count to get the answers to addition problems. But counting takes too much time. You can work faster if you have memorized the addition facts. Do this exercise without counting. Check your answers. Study the facts you missed until you can do this exercise with no errors.

PRACTICE 5

Solve.

1.
$$\begin{array}{cccccccccc} 6 & 8 & 4 & 8 & 1 & 5 & 6 & 3 & 7 & 2 \\ +7 & +3 & +2 & +7 & +2 & +1 & +9 & +8 & +0 & +7 \end{array}$$

2.
$$\begin{array}{cccccccccc} 6 & 5 & 2 & 7 & 9 & 9 & 5 & 3 & 1 & 0 \\ +4 & +8 & +5 & +6 & +3 & +0 & +2 & +9 & +8 & +3 \end{array}$$

3.
$$\begin{array}{ccccccccccc} 9 & 7 & 4 & 3 & 4 & 3 & 9 & 7 & 1 & 7 \\ +7 & +2 & +4 & +5 & +6 & +7 & +1 & +5 & +6 & +7 \end{array}$$

4.
$$\begin{array}{ccccccccccc} 8 & 9 & 1 & 0 & 4 & 6 & 1 & 3 & 5 & 6 \\ +1 & +6 & +3 & +2 & +9 & +2 & +4 & +3 & +3 & +5 \end{array}$$

5.
$$\begin{array}{ccccccccccc} 9 & 4 & 8 & 1 & 7 & 5 & 9 & 8 & 4 & 7 \\ +2 & +1 & +8 & +5 & +3 & +9 & +4 & +0 & +7 & +9 \end{array}$$

6.
$$\begin{array}{ccccccccccc} 2 & 9 & 6 & 6 & 3 & 2 & 1 & 7 & 8 & 5 \\ +2 & +5 & +1 & +0 & +2 & +4 & +1 & +8 & +2 & +0 \end{array}$$

7.
$$\begin{array}{ccccccccccc} 4 & 5 & 3 & 9 & 2 & 5 & 7 & 6 & 2 & 3 \\ +8 & +5 & +6 & +8 & +9 & +6 & +1 & +3 & +6 & +1 \end{array}$$

8.
$$\begin{array}{ccccccccccc} 2 & 1 & 2 & 6 & 5 & 2 & 0 & 8 & 4 & 9 \\ +3 & +9 & +8 & +6 & +4 & +1 & +1 & +4 & +3 & +9 \end{array}$$

9.
$$\begin{array}{ccccccccccc} 6 & 4 & 1 & 5 & 4 & 8 & 3 & 5 & 7 & 8 \\ +8 & +5 & +7 & +6 & +0 & +5 & +4 & +7 & +4 & +6 \end{array}$$

10.
$$\begin{array}{ccccccccccc} 6 & 3 & 9 & 2 & 8 & 4 & 5 & 3 & 2 & 7 \\ +1 & +5 & +4 & +3 & +2 & +8 & +9 & +7 & +6 & +9 \end{array}$$

To check your answers, turn to page 107.

Whole Numbers

Addition of Larger Numbers

Discount Warehouse has opened its doors for job applicants. On Monday, 73 applicants applied for full-time jobs. Another 25 applicants applied for part-time jobs. Find the total number of applicants.

The answer to an addition problem is called the **sum** or **total**. You can find the sum of large numbers using the basic addition facts. Begin by adding all the numbers in the ones column. Then add the numbers in the tens column. Continue working to the left, adding each column until you have finished.

Example: 73 + 25 =

STEP 1.   Add the ones: 3 + 5 = 8.

STEP 2.   Add the tens: 7 + 2 = 9.

$$\begin{array}{r} 73 \\ + 25 \\ \hline 98 \end{array}$$

⟹ The total number of applicants was 98.

To check an addition problem, add from the bottom to the top. The new sum should be the same as the old sum.

Add the ones from the bottom: 5 + 3 = 8. Then add the tens from the bottom: 2 + 7 = 9. Again the total is 98.

$$\begin{array}{r} 98 \\ 73 \\ + 25 \\ \hline 98 \end{array}$$

PRACTICE 6

A. Add and check.

1.
$$\begin{array}{r} 52 \\ + 34 \end{array} \qquad \begin{array}{r} 60 \\ + 29 \end{array} \qquad \begin{array}{r} 45 \\ + 42 \end{array} \qquad \begin{array}{r} 82 \\ + 17 \end{array} \qquad \begin{array}{r} 12 \\ + 63 \end{array} \qquad \begin{array}{r} 51 \\ + 40 \end{array} \qquad \begin{array}{r} 28 \\ + 51 \end{array}$$

2.
$$\begin{array}{r} 56 \\ + 20 \end{array} \qquad \begin{array}{r} 72 \\ + 11 \end{array} \qquad \begin{array}{r} 34 \\ + 53 \end{array} \qquad \begin{array}{r} 12 \\ + 66 \end{array} \qquad \begin{array}{r} 50 \\ + 47 \end{array} \qquad \begin{array}{r} 48 \\ + 21 \end{array} \qquad \begin{array}{r} 63 \\ + 34 \end{array}$$

3. $\begin{array}{r} 264 \\ + 334 \\ \hline \end{array}$ $\quad$ $\begin{array}{r} 516 \\ + 402 \\ \hline \end{array}$ $\quad$ $\begin{array}{r} 122 \\ + 553 \\ \hline \end{array}$ $\quad$ $\begin{array}{r} 525 \\ + 273 \\ \hline \end{array}$ $\quad$ $\begin{array}{r} 862 \\ + 116 \\ \hline \end{array}$ $\quad$ $\begin{array}{r} 403 \\ + 293 \\ \hline \end{array}$

4. $\begin{array}{r} 542 \\ + 156 \\ \hline \end{array}$ $\quad$ $\begin{array}{r} 635 \\ + 342 \\ \hline \end{array}$ $\quad$ $\begin{array}{r} 246 \\ + 540 \\ \hline \end{array}$ $\quad$ $\begin{array}{r} 508 \\ + 271 \\ \hline \end{array}$ $\quad$ $\begin{array}{r} 330 \\ + 364 \\ \hline \end{array}$ $\quad$ $\begin{array}{r} 526 \\ + 271 \\ \hline \end{array}$

5. $\begin{array}{r} 7,396 \\ + 2,002 \\ \hline \end{array}$ $\quad$ $\begin{array}{r} 5,032 \\ + 4,936 \\ \hline \end{array}$ $\quad$ $\begin{array}{r} 6,717 \\ + 3,230 \\ \hline \end{array}$ $\quad$ $\begin{array}{r} 4,204 \\ + 3,772 \\ \hline \end{array}$ $\quad$ $\begin{array}{r} 3,276 \\ + 2,611 \\ \hline \end{array}$

6. $\begin{array}{r} 41,038 \\ + 38,701 \\ \hline \end{array}$ $\quad$ $\begin{array}{r} 35,926 \\ + 42,053 \\ \hline \end{array}$ $\quad$ $\begin{array}{r} 45,228 \\ + 21,621 \\ \hline \end{array}$ $\quad$ $\begin{array}{r} 20,593 \\ + 46,205 \\ \hline \end{array}$ $\quad$ $\begin{array}{r} 74,523 \\ + 12,436 \\ \hline \end{array}$

7. $\begin{array}{r} 641,803 \\ + 326,105 \\ \hline \end{array}$ $\quad$ $\begin{array}{r} 281,904 \\ + 118,092 \\ \hline \end{array}$ $\quad$ $\begin{array}{r} 572,683 \\ + 326,214 \\ \hline \end{array}$ $\quad$ $\begin{array}{r} 746,105 \\ + 230,842 \\ \hline \end{array}$

If an addition problem is written horizontally (with the numbers going across from left to right), rewrite the problem. Put the ones under the ones, the tens under the tens, and so on.

Example: 325 + 64 =

Step 1. Rewrite the problem.	$\begin{array}{r} 325 \\ + 64 \\ \hline 389 \end{array}$
Step 2. 5 + 4 = 9	
Step 3. 2 + 6 = 8	
Step 4. 3 + nothing = 3	

Whole Numbers

B. Add and check.

8. $86 + 512 =$ $\qquad$ $316 + 72 =$ $\qquad$ $31 + 527 =$

9. $704 + 63 =$ $\qquad$ $25 + 952 =$ $\qquad$ $608 + 91 =$

10. $3,417 + 152 =$ $\qquad$ $861 + 5,014 =$ $\qquad$ $4,820 + 136 =$

11. $205 + 6,273 =$ $\qquad$ $8,103 + 443 =$ $\qquad$ $627 + 9,052 =$

12. The main floor of the Rialto Theatre has 482 seats. The balcony has 207 seats. Find the total number of seats in the theatre.

13. The Central Tool and Die Company has 526 day-shift workers and 253 night-shift workers. Find the total number of employees.

14. Midvale Community College has 927 full-time students and 1,061 part-time students. Altogether how many students attend the college?

15. In Sara's first week at the East Midvale Nursery, she sold 23 lemon trees and 54 flowering plum trees. How many trees did Sara sell in all?

16. The Ticor Building has two office suites for rent. The first office has 835 square feet and the second has 1,040 square feet. What is the total square footage of the two office spaces?

To check your answers, turn to page 107.

Addition with Carrying

On Saturday 956 people attended the Midvale Fair. On Sunday 847 people attended. What was the combined attendance for the two days?

When the sum of the digit in a column is a two-digit number, *carry* the digit at the left to the next column to the left.

Example: 956 + 847 =

STEP 1. Add the ones: 6 + 7 = 13. Write 3 under the ones column, and carry the 1 to the tens column. The 1 is one ten. It must be added to the tens column.

$$\begin{array}{r} \overset{1\,1}{9}56 \\ +\ \ 847 \\ \hline 1{,}803 \end{array}$$

STEP 2. Add the tens: 1 + 5 = 6 and 6 + 4 = 10. Write the zero under the tens, and carry the 1 to the hundreds column.

STEP 3. Add the hundreds: 1 + 9 = 10 and 10 + 8 = 18.

➠ The combined attendance for the two days was 1,803.

PRACTICE 7

Add and check.

1.

16	48	75	83	67	28	57
+ 94	+ 65	+ 78	+ 49	+ 66	+ 42	+ 53

2.

94	82	35	47	56	13	82
+ 37	+ 59	+ 89	+ 64	+ 86	+ 29	+ 88

3.

56	88	54	77	35	61	58
+ 79	+ 95	+ 46	+ 38	+ 27	+ 89	+ 46

4.

97	54	48	19	47	34	66
+ 73	+ 68	+ 93	+ 36	+ 57	+ 96	+ 57

5.

782	349	493	672	781	389
+ 38	+ 73	+ 29	+ 48	+ 79	+ 66

6.

24	48	88	18	93	59
+ 297	+ 653	+ 842	+ 786	+ 577	+ 693

7.

492	298	536	493	687	652
+ 729	+ 436	+ 785	+ 608	+ 479	+ 388

8.

545	687	364	152	749	198
+ 667	+ 593	+ 488	+ 759	+ 382	+ 907

9.

6,082	2,945	3,920	8,224	4,986
+ 4,920	+ 1,580	+ 8,672	+ 3,257	+ 6,549

10.

7,853	5,588	3,216	2,768	4,126
+ 4,831	+ 6,347	+ 2,268	+ 5,936	+ 7,077

11.   861,560   802,644   716,636   879,120
    + 647,347   + 873,447   + 732,199   + 421,976

Rewrite and then add.

12. 4,821 + 475 =   3,276 + 267 =   3,081 + 569 =

13. 275 + 1,926 =   554 + 4,827 =   659 + 3,732 =

14. 87,614 + 5,709 =   72,859 + 5,683 =   48,109 + 2,749 =

15. 6,147 + 27,948 =   8,665 + 27,948 =   2,766 + 45,339 =

Solve the following.

16. The distance from Philadelphia to New York is 92 miles. The distance from New York to Boston is 187 miles. What is the distance from Philadelphia to Boston by way of New York?

17. In June the Music Center sold 2,986 CDs and in July they sold 3,029 CDs. What total number of CDs did the store sell in June and July?

18. In 1950 the population of Johnstown was 18,207. In 1995 there were 36,981 more people in Johnstown than in 1950. What was the population of Johnstown in 1995?

19. In the 1990 census, Manhattan had a population of 1,487,536. Brooklyn had 923,020 more people than Manhattan. Find the population of Brooklyn in 1990.

To check your answers, turn to page 108.

Whole Numbers

Adding Money

On her way to work, Sabrina bought a magazine for $3 and a packet of envelopes for $1.29. What was the total of her purchases?

Dollars and cents are separated by the decimal point. But adding money amounts is the same as adding whole numbers. Just remember to line up pennies under pennies, dimes under dimes, and dollars under dollars as you set up the problem.

Example: $3 + $1.29 =

STEP 1.   Rewrite the problem. Notice that $3 goes left of the decimal point. Use zeros to hold the dimes and pennies places.

dollars ——┐ ┌—— dimes
          │ │ ┌—— pennies
          ↓ ↓↓

$3.00
+ 1.29
———————
$4.29

STEP 2.   Add each column.

⟹   The total of Sabrina's purchases was $4.29.

PRACTICE 8

Solve.

1. $3.98 + $15 =   65¢ + $2.95 = $20 + $4.15 =

2. $.89 + $.06 = $19.98 + $4 = $5 + 89¢ =

3. $249 + $8.40 = $1.09 + 79¢ = $29.98 + $1.02 =

4. In May the Chans paid $465 for rent and $87.36 for utilities. What was the total of these expenses?

5. Fred bought a cordless screwdriver on sale for $24. The sales tax on the screwdriver was $1.68. What was the total price including tax?

6. Arlette bought a pair of hiking boots on sale for $69.99. Before the sale the boots cost $15 more. What was the price of the boots before the sale?

7. Art took his family on a weekend camping trip. He spent $56.95 for food and supplies to take on the trip. Gasoline cost $38. How much did Art spend on the weekend trip?

To check your answers, turn to page 108.

Addition with More than Two Numbers

Soren works in the shipping department of a mail order company. He packed three boxes for one customer. One box weighed 38 pounds, another weighed 16 pounds, and the third weighed 9 pounds. What was the combined weight of the three packages?

To add more than two numbers, find the total for each column. The digits in a column can be added in any order.

Example: $38 + 16 + 9 =$

STEP 1.   Line up the numbers and add the digits in the units column. $8 + 6 = 14$. Then $14 + 9 = 23$. Write 3 in the units column and carry 2 to the tens.

$$\begin{array}{r} 2 \\ 38 \\ 16 \\ +\ 9 \\ \hline 63 \end{array}$$

STEP 2.   Add the digits in the tens column: $2 + 3 = 5$. Then $5 + 1 = 6$.

⟱   The combined weight of the packages was 63 pounds.

PRACTICE 9

Solve.

1.

93	73	28	97	58	90	13
15	56	39	40	70	21	25
+ 72	+ 71	+ 60	+ 23	+ 65	+ 39	+ 86

2.

979	577	522	391	258	174
628	639	839	674	229	848
+ 657	+ 381	+ 464	+ 545	+ 652	+ 702

3.

393	217	565	163	413	359
578	556	692	433	780	142
+ 643	+ 897	+ 509	+ 195	+ 629	+ 748

4.

746	332	316	754	991	580
879	821	841	440	654	814
380	285	972	575	262	562
+ 903	+ 394	+ 343	+ 651	+ 373	+ 735

5.

87,614	72,859	48,109	27,948	83,443
5,709	5,683	2,749	6,147	8,665
+ 25,338	+ 45,012	+ 19,172	+ 20,482	+ 11,626

6.

75,856	97,883	42,885	45,984	95,413
10,184	42,130	77,324	47,483	20,766
+ 32,859	+ 87,949	+ 96,012	+ 71,573	+ 45,129

7.
755	213	248	117	929	155
570	527	340	223	913	568
664	431	337	704	857	788
421	127	974	978	582	321
+ 853	+ 965	+ 132	+ 491	+ 766	+ 347

8.
120	655	483	727	382	586
45	27	58	63	54	43
8	9	4	7	6	2
617	548	387	854	431	920
+ 21	+ 37	+ 73	+ 45	+ 96	+ 97

9.
861,560	802,644	716,636	879,120
647,347	873,117	732,199	421,976
+ 621,175	+ 544,623	+ 240,835	+ 782,442

10.
984,406	942,532	375,541	279,615
838,459	639,617	509,148	566,420
+ 974,302	+ 483,336	+ 382,936	+ 713,995

11. $237 + 5,465 + 32 =$ $16 + 8,645 + 521 =$

12. $9,048 + 27 + 376 =$ $394 + 18 + 2,506 =$

13. $68 + 587 + 13 + 247 =$ $232 + 65 + 534 + 18 =$

14. $836 + 17 + 5 + 6,207 =$ $87 + 980 + 3 + 212 =$

15. $12 + 9{,}684 + 31 + 275 =$ $\qquad$ $237 + 75 + 4{,}360 + 42 =$

16. $989 + 7 + 8{,}876 + 14 =$ $\qquad$ $1{,}596 + 17 + 393 + 66 =$

17. $663 + 75{,}432 + 18 =$ $\qquad$ $93{,}262 + 84 + 516 =$

18. $7{,}966 + 457 + 49{,}462 =$ $\qquad$ $844 + 17{,}008 + 4{,}936 =$

19. For breakfast Jack ate scrambled eggs (250 calories), bacon (100 calories), buttered toast (85 calories), and coffee with cream (30 calories). What was the total number of calories in Jack's breakfast?

20. Ethan is weighing baggage and boxes before loading the items on a small plane. A large box weighs 168 pounds. A smaller one weighs 127 pounds. Three suitcases weigh 86, 63, and 50 pounds. Find the total weight of the five items.

21. During one week a salesperson earned the following commissions: Monday, $48.50; Tuesday, $29.65; Wednesday, $19.80; Thursday, $44; and Friday, $32.20. What were the total commissions for the week?

22. Attending day classes at Central Business School are 1,028 men and 970 women. At night there are 937 men and 864 women. How many people attend classes at Central?

23. Tony's Corner Restaurant made $218.29 on Friday. They made $293.47 on Saturday. They made $167.32 on Sunday. How much did they make over those three days?

24. During a recent election for the mayor of Midvale, Mr. Jones got 34,207 votes. Mr. Smith got 21,963 votes. Mr. Miller got 12,294 votes. Find the total number of votes for these three.

25. Fred's employer makes the following deductions from his paycheck: $72.48 for Social Security, $80.19 for federal income tax, and $50.76 for state income tax. Find the total of these deductions.

26. At Metropolitan Hospital 276 employees work from 8:00 in the morning until 4:00 in the afternoon. Another 193 employees work from 4:00 in the afternoon until midnight, and 118 employees work from midnight until 8:00 in the morning. What is the total number of employees at the hospital?

Watch out for extra numbers. In problem 26, make sure you add only the numbers of employees. In problem 27, add only the money amounts.

27. Petra bought a 28-ounce jar of peanut butter for $2.29, an 8-ounce bottle of salad dressing for 89¢, and a 16-ounce container of cottage cheese for $1.39. What was the total cost of her purchases?

28. When Raymond took his car to be serviced at a garage, he had to pay $109.88 for complete brake service, $18.49 for a new shock absorber, and $24.98 for a front end alignment. Find the total for these items.

29. This year the Donaldson family pays $524.60 a month for rent. Next year the landlord will charge them a monthly increase of $23.61 plus an additional monthly charge of $3 for the new windows he installed. What will be their monthly rent next year?

30. The populations of the three largest U.S. cities are: New York 7,322,564; Los Angeles, 3,485,398; and Chicago, 2,783,726. What is the combined population of these three cities?

To check your answers, turn to page 109.

ADDITION REVIEW

The problems on this page and the next page will help you find out if you need to review the addition unit of this book. Solve the problems. When you finish, look at the progress chart to see which pages you should review.

1. $\begin{array}{r} 436 \\ + 253 \\ \hline \end{array}$

2. $\begin{array}{r} 3,504 \\ + 1,283 \\ \hline \end{array}$

3. $\begin{array}{r} 650,335 \\ + 249,234 \\ \hline \end{array}$

4. 813 + 72 =

5. 63 + 825 =

6. 3,426 + 80,261 =

7. $\begin{array}{r} 57 \\ + 96 \\ \hline \end{array}$

8. $\begin{array}{r} 736 \\ + 597 \\ \hline \end{array}$

9. $\begin{array}{r} 2,953 \\ + 9,227 \\ \hline \end{array}$

10. $\begin{array}{r} 4,923 \\ + 8,117 \\ \hline \end{array}$

11. 6,374 + 588 =

12. 9,291 + 18,688 =

13. $24 + $9.75 =

14. 98¢ + $12.85 =

15. 5,102 + 36 + 3,977 =

16. 8 + 23 + 9,451 + 3,285 =

17. In the morning Mr. Miller drove 84 miles. In the afternoon he drove 106 miles. In the evening he drove 77 miles. How far did Mr. Miller drive that day?

18. In 1930 the population of Troy was 11,257. In 1995 there were 29,583 more people in Troy than in 1930. What was Troy's population in 1995?

19. Moe bought an electric drill for $54.95 and a set of drill bits for $4.37. He paid $7.49 in sales tax on these items. What was the total amount of his bill?

20. The Midvale Community Organization held a three-day festival. On Friday 692 people came to the festival. On Saturday 1,056 people came. On Sunday there were 947 people. What was the total attendance for the three days?

PROGRESS CHECK

Check your answers on page 109. Then return to the review pages for the problems you missed. Correct your answers before going on to the next unit.

If you missed problems	Review pages
1, 2, 3, 4, 5, or 6	21 to 23
7, 8, 9, 10, 11, 12, or 18	24 to 26
13 or 14	27
15, 16, 17, 18, 19, or 20	28 to 32

Subtraction

Subtraction Facts

It takes too much time to count to get the answers to subtraction problems. You can work faster if you have memorized the subtraction facts. Do this exercise without counting. Check your answers. Then study the facts you missed until you can do this exercise with no errors.

PRACTICE 10

Solve.

1.
14	2	5	8	6	16	13	8	1
− 5	− 1	− 2	− 4	− 1	− 7	− 8	− 7	− 1

2.
16	9	11	8	3	12	11	13	15
− 9	− 7	− 3	− 1	− 3	− 8	− 6	− 5	− 6

3.
5	10	4	11	7	7	9	4	10
− 4	− 2	− 2	− 9	− 6	− 3	− 2	− 4	− 9

4.
13	10	16	7	8	15	11	9	2
− 6	− 3	− 8	− 1	− 5	− 7	− 7	− 1	− 2

5.
9	6	9	12	10	3	10	9	12
− 3	− 2	− 9	− 9	− 7	− 2	− 4	− 6	− 6

6.
6	11	10	17	14	12	8	12	11
− 3	− 2	− 1	− 9	− 9	− 7	− 8	− 4	− 8

7.
11	8	6	7	12	15	13	14	9
− 5	− 2	− 6	− 4	− 3	− 9	− 4	− 6	− 4

8.
17	7	9	8	11	4	15	18	7
− 8	− 5	− 5	− 6	− 4	− 1	− 8	− 9	− 2

9.
12	5	13	9	10	14	8	10	5
− 5	− 3	− 9	− 8	− 5	− 7	− 3	− 8	− 5

10.
5	6	10	4	7	13	14	3	8
− 1	− 4	− 6	− 3	− 7	− 7	− 8	− 1	− 0

To check your answers, turn to page 109.

Subtraction of Larger Numbers

There are 73 workers at the Ajax Container Company. Of these, 21 are in sales. How many of the workers at Ajax are not in sales?

The answer to a subtraction problem is called the **difference.** You can find the difference between two numbers with the basic subtraction facts. Begin by subtracting the ones. Then subtract the tens. Continue to subtract each column until you have finished.

Example: $73 - 21 =$

STEP 1.   Subtract the ones: $3 - 1 = 2$.

STEP 2.   Subtract the tens: $7 - 2 = 5$.

$$\begin{array}{r} 73 \\ -\ 21 \\ \hline 52 \end{array}$$

➠   52 workers at the company are not in sales.

To check a subtraction problem, add the answer (the difference) to the lower number in the original problem. The sum should equal the top number.
To check the example, add 21 + 52.

$$\begin{array}{r} 73 \\ -\ 21 \\ \hline 52 \end{array} \qquad \begin{array}{r} 21 \\ +\ 52 \\ \hline 73 \end{array} \begin{array}{l} \text{lower number} \\ \text{difference} \\ \text{top number} \end{array}$$

PRACTICE 11

Subtract and check.

1.
$$\begin{array}{r} 74 \\ -\ 23 \end{array} \qquad \begin{array}{r} 93 \\ -\ 72 \end{array} \qquad \begin{array}{r} 58 \\ -\ 28 \end{array} \qquad \begin{array}{r} 82 \\ -\ 32 \end{array} \qquad \begin{array}{r} 95 \\ -\ 63 \end{array} \qquad \begin{array}{r} 56 \\ -\ 15 \end{array} \qquad \begin{array}{r} 57 \\ -\ 54 \end{array}$$

2.
$$\begin{array}{r} 466 \\ -\ 53 \end{array} \qquad \begin{array}{r} 583 \\ -\ 82 \end{array} \qquad \begin{array}{r} 287 \\ -\ 65 \end{array} \qquad \begin{array}{r} 384 \\ -\ 44 \end{array} \qquad \begin{array}{r} 637 \\ -\ 21 \end{array} \qquad \begin{array}{r} 954 \\ -\ 33 \end{array}$$

3.

747	739	388	455	873	674
− 233	− 607	− 185	− 251	− 660	− 413

4.

3,453	9,358	6,917	7,617	8,904
− 351	− 244	− 805	− 513	− 702

5.

5,397	5,472	3,874	9,198	8,614
− 2,093	− 4,160	− 1,273	− 8,092	− 5,212

6.

73,156	79,048	21,859	57,740	35,048
− 23,104	− 66,025	− 10,348	− 26,520	− 24,016

Rewrite each problem. Then subtract and check.

7. $679 - 52 =$ $856 - 41 =$ $674 - 34 =$

8. $784 - 603 =$ $467 - 346 =$ $575 - 271 =$

9. $1,793 - 683 =$ $7,605 - 401 =$ $6,234 - 132 =$

10. $7,279 - 6,258 =$ $4,833 - 3,401 =$ $3,986 - 2,751 =$

11. Lorraine wants to sell 98 pairs of pants in one week to break the store record for sales. She has already sold 67 pairs. How many more does she need to sell to break the record?

12. There were 576 people who signed up to attend a convention in Atlantic City. Of these, 425 people actually attended. How many people did not attend?

13. Ohio became a state in 1803. For how many years had Ohio been a state by 1995?

To check your answers, turn to page 110.

Regrouping

Manny works in the shipping department of a company that makes welding equipment. In the morning there were 74 packages of welding rods to be shipped. By noon Manny had wrapped and labeled 58 packages. How many packages were left?

When the bottom number in any column is too large to subtract from the top number, you must **regroup** the top number. You may know this operation as *renaming* or *borrowing*.

Example: $74 - 58 =$

You can also show regrouping like this:

STEP 1. 8 is too large to subtract from 4. Regroup the top number. Take 1 ten from the tens column $(7 - 1 = 6)$ and add it to the units $(10 + 4 = 14)$.

$$\begin{array}{r} {}^{6}\llap{/}7{}^{14}\llap{/}4 \\ -\ 58 \\ \hline 16 \end{array}$$

$$\begin{array}{r} {}^{6}7{}_{1}4 \\ -\ 58 \\ \hline 16 \end{array}$$

STEP 2. Subtract the units: $14 - 8 = 6$.

STEP 3. Subtract the tens: $6 - 5 = 1$.

STEP 4. Check: $58 + 16 = 74$.

⟾ There were 16 packages of rods left.

PRACTICE 12

A. Subtract and check.

1.
$$\begin{array}{r} 82 \\ -\ 9 \\ \hline \end{array} \qquad \begin{array}{r} 51 \\ -\ 8 \\ \hline \end{array} \qquad \begin{array}{r} 65 \\ -\ 7 \\ \hline \end{array} \qquad \begin{array}{r} 56 \\ -\ 8 \\ \hline \end{array} \qquad \begin{array}{r} 92 \\ -\ 4 \\ \hline \end{array} \qquad \begin{array}{r} 74 \\ -\ 5 \\ \hline \end{array} \qquad \begin{array}{r} 36 \\ -\ 7 \\ \hline \end{array}$$

2.
$$\begin{array}{r} 76 \\ -\ 9 \\ \hline \end{array} \qquad \begin{array}{r} 81 \\ -\ 7 \\ \hline \end{array} \qquad \begin{array}{r} 34 \\ -\ 5 \\ \hline \end{array} \qquad \begin{array}{r} 73 \\ -\ 6 \\ \hline \end{array} \qquad \begin{array}{r} 28 \\ -\ 9 \\ \hline \end{array} \qquad \begin{array}{r} 95 \\ -\ 8 \\ \hline \end{array} \qquad \begin{array}{r} 44 \\ -\ 5 \\ \hline \end{array}$$

3.
$$\begin{array}{r} 23 \\ -\ 18 \\ \hline \end{array} \qquad \begin{array}{r} 71 \\ -\ 62 \\ \hline \end{array} \qquad \begin{array}{r} 86 \\ -\ 28 \\ \hline \end{array} \qquad \begin{array}{r} 42 \\ -\ 37 \\ \hline \end{array} \qquad \begin{array}{r} 93 \\ -\ 19 \\ \hline \end{array} \qquad \begin{array}{r} 81 \\ -\ 64 \\ \hline \end{array} \qquad \begin{array}{r} 68 \\ -\ 49 \\ \hline \end{array}$$

4.
$$\begin{array}{r} 31 \\ -\ 17 \\ \hline \end{array} \qquad \begin{array}{r} 45 \\ -\ 29 \\ \hline \end{array} \qquad \begin{array}{r} 72 \\ -\ 16 \\ \hline \end{array} \qquad \begin{array}{r} 63 \\ -\ 38 \\ \hline \end{array} \qquad \begin{array}{r} 47 \\ -\ 29 \\ \hline \end{array} \qquad \begin{array}{r} 74 \\ -\ 55 \\ \hline \end{array} \qquad \begin{array}{r} 93 \\ -\ 47 \\ \hline \end{array}$$

In some problems you will need to regroup several times. Study the following example carefully.

Example: Subtract 1,389 from 3,567.

$$\begin{array}{r} \overset{15}{} \\ \overset{4\,\cancel{5}\,17}{} \\ 3,\cancel{5}\cancel{6}\cancel{7} \\ -\ 1,389 \\ \hline 2,178 \end{array} \qquad \textit{Check:} \quad \begin{array}{r} 1,389 \\ +\ 2,178 \\ \hline 3,567 \end{array}$$

Notice that you do not have to regroup the 3 in the thousands column. You can subtract the hundreds (4 − 3 = 1) without regrouping.

B. Subtract and check.

5.
$$\begin{array}{r} 955 \\ -\ 66 \\ \hline \end{array} \qquad \begin{array}{r} 680 \\ -\ 91 \\ \hline \end{array} \qquad \begin{array}{r} 277 \\ -\ 98 \\ \hline \end{array} \qquad \begin{array}{r} 712 \\ -\ 24 \\ \hline \end{array} \qquad \begin{array}{r} 256 \\ -\ 78 \\ \hline \end{array} \qquad \begin{array}{r} 364 \\ -\ 95 \\ \hline \end{array}$$

6.

671	582	363	724	386	450
− 286	− 493	− 265	− 328	− 199	− 278

7.

366	655	612	248	521	673
− 294	− 483	− 470	− 156	− 380	− 592

8.

7,451	3,256	2,374	6,853	8,672
− 2,863	− 1,477	− 1,675	− 2,964	− 3,884

9.

52,640	71,158	84,932	46,123	88,534
− 12,836	− 25,560	− 44,871	− 29,302	− 29,317

10.

869,356	278,925	643,871	734,843
− 97,488	− 89,536	− 50,683	− 45,294

11.

427,731	588,326	872,385	427,618
− 138,855	− 369,748	− 487,638	− 239,729

Rewrite, subtract, and check.

12. 2,812 − 58 =   4,427 − 519 =   2,116 − 1,098 =

13. 5,850 − 936 =   2,471 − 1,095 =   6,327 − 89 =

14. 5,173 − 4,158 =   2,269 − 290 =   6,478 − 3,582 =

15. 8,741 − 6,197 =   2,450 − 1,185 =   5,633 − 4,946 =

16. 86,853 − 976 =   47,265 − 8,037 =   61,722 − 938 =

17. 62,982 − 8,793 =   63,124 − 496 =   56,138 − 9,359 =

18. 54,362 − 9,955 =   61,339 − 876 =   48,872 − 19,886 =

19. 69,155 − 4,936 =   77,864 − 9,238 =   34,091 − 7,342 =

Give the answers to the next problems the correct labels such as *$* or *people*.

20. The Andersons must drive 482 miles to get to their son's house. They stop for lunch after they drive 219 miles. How much farther do they have to drive?

21. There are 612 seats in the Midvale High School auditorium. At a performance of a school play, 43 seats were empty. How many people were in the audience?

22. A CD player once sold for $245. It is now on sale for $219. How much can Alba save if she buys the CD player on sale?

23. Last month the Acevedo family took home $1,732.19. Their bills for the month amounted to $1,584.26. How much money did they have left for the month after paying all their bills?

24. Mr. Vlastos made $22,756 last year. His wife made $29,332 last year. How much more did Mrs. Vlastos make than her husband?

To check your answers, turn to page 110.

Regrouping with Zeros

Kareem had $802 in his checking account. How much was left after he wrote a check for $539?

To regroup with zeros, look at the first digit that is not zero in the top number.

Example: $802 - 539 =$

STEP 1. You cannot subtract 9 from 2. Take 1 hundred from the hundreds column $(8 - 1 = 7)$. You now have 10 tens in the tens column.

$$\begin{array}{r} 7\ 10 \\ 8\!\!\!\not0\,2 \\ -\ 539 \\ \hline \end{array}$$

STEP 2. Take 1 ten from the 10 in the tens column $(10 - 1 = 9)$ and add it to the units $(10 + 2 = 12)$.

$$\begin{array}{r} 9 \\ 7\ 10\ 12 \\ 8\!\!\!\not0\,2 \\ -\ 539 \\ \hline 263 \end{array}$$

STEP 3. Subtract the units: $12 - 9 = 3$.

STEP 4. Subtract the tens: $9 - 3 = 6$.

STEP 5. Subtract the hundreds: $7 - 5 = 2$.

STEP 6. Check. $539 + 263 = 802$.

➠ Kareem had $263 left in his account.

PRACTICE 13

A. Subtract and check.

1. 501	908	306	707	805	208
− 37	− 59	− 77	− 98	− 88	− 19

2. 306	604	503	701	308	902
− 57	− 85	− 64	− 36	− 79	− 84

3.
307	206	704	903	506	401
− 98	− 57	− 66	− 75	− 29	− 42

4.
208	304	906	508	703	406
− 159	− 215	− 667	− 349	− 256	− 118

In some problems you must regroup several times. Study the next example carefully.

Example: $8,002 - 2,563 =$

STEP 1. You cannot subtract 3 from 2. Take 1 thousand from the thousands column ($8 - 1 = 7$). You now have 10 hundreds in the hundreds column.

$$\begin{array}{r} 7\,10 \\ 8{,}002 \\ -\,2{,}563 \end{array}$$

STEP 2. Take 1 hundred from the 10 in the hundreds column ($10 - 1 = 9$) and put it in the tens column.

$$\begin{array}{r} 9 \\ 7\,10\,10 \\ 8{,}002 \\ -\,2{,}563 \end{array}$$

STEP 3. Take 1 ten from the 10 in the tens column ($10 - 1 = 9$) and add it to the units ($10 + 2 = 12$).

$$\begin{array}{r} 9\ \ 9 \\ 7\,10\,10\,12 \\ 8{,}002 \\ -\,2{,}563 \\ \hline 5{,}439 \end{array}$$

STEP 4. Subtract the units: $12 - 3 = 9$.

STEP 5. Subtract the tens: $9 - 6 = 3$.

STEP 6. Subtract the hundreds: $9 - 5 = 4$.

STEP 7. Subtract the thousands: $7 - 2 = 5$.

STEP 8. Check. $2,563 + 5,439 = 8,002$.

B. Subtract and check.

5.
800	700	200	500	600	400
− 46	− 27	− 93	− 66	− 59	− 81

6.

900	300	800	700	500	600
− 133	− 259	− 615	− 477	− 286	− 138

7.

8,070	9,020	6,050	4,030	7,010
− 3,586	− 2,974	− 3,266	− 1,253	− 4,865

8.

9,003	5,004	8,006	3,005	6,002
− 2,341	− 4,860	− 3,975	− 1,263	− 4,891

9.

7,008	5,004	3,003	4,002	6,001
− 3,749	− 2,518	− 1,124	− 3,207	− 2,553

10.

6,000	9,000	4,000	8,000	2,000
− 352	− 481	− 296	− 337	− 452

11.

2,000	3,000	9,000	7,000	6,000
− 1,234	− 1,597	− 1,945	− 2,366	− 1,007

12.

50,600	50,030	40,008	70,050	23,000
− 2,387	− 6,429	− 3,557	− 4,928	− 1,820

13.

82,006	90,007	40,700	32,004	50,030
− 41,235	− 73,492	− 11,658	− 19,726	− 37,024

Rewrite, subtract, and check.

14. $3,040 - 856 =$ $6,070 - 987 =$ $3,080 - 485 =$

15. $3,005 - 584 =$ $8,006 - 322 =$ $5,001 - 2,301 =$

16. $9,000 - 466 =$ $7,000 - 370 =$ $3,000 - 259 =$

17. $30,050 - 2,946 =$ $40,600 - 3,872 =$ $70,002 - 6,071 =$

18. $52,000 - 4,905 =$ $90,072 - 5,781 =$ $40,300 - 9,243 =$

Remember to line up money problems with pennies under pennies, dimes under dimes, and dollars under dollars.

Example: $\$20 - \$16.90 =$

STEP 1.   Put a decimal point and two zeros
for the dimes and pennies in $20.

STEP 2.   Regroup and subtract.

STEP 3.   Check. $\$16.90 + \$3.10 = \$20.00.$

$$
\begin{array}{r}
9 \\
1\,\cancel{1}\!\cancel{0}\,10 \\
\$20.00 \\
-\ \ 16.90 \\
\hline
\$3.10
\end{array}
$$

C. Give each answer the correct label such as *$* or *people*.

19. Jeff bought a new shirt for $26.79. How much change did he get from $30?

20. Mount McKinley in Alaska is 20,320 feet high. Mount Whitney in California is 14,494 feet high. How much higher is Mount McKinley than Mount Whitney?

21. The Murrays are buying a house for $118,500. They made a down payment of $17,775. They will pay the rest of the price of the house with a mortgage. What is the amount of the mortgage?

22. Mary makes $485 a week. Her employer deducts $101.85 for taxes and social security. What is her weekly take-home pay?

23. A neighborhood community center wants to raise $100,000 to renovate their meeting hall. After six months the center has raised $61,093. How much more money do they need?

24. Fred borrowed $6,500 to buy a used truck. He has paid back $2,125. How much does he still owe?

25. The record attendance at Central Stadium is 82,043 people. Last fall the greatest attendance was 78,956 people. Find the difference between last fall's greatest attendance and the record.

26. In 1960 there were 3,962,000 farms in the U.S. In 1993 the number of farms was 2,068,000. How many fewer farms were there in 1993 than in 1960?

27. The highest mountain in the world is Mount Everest with an elevation of 29,108 feet. The highest point in North America is Mount McKinley with an elevation of 20,320 feet. What is the difference in their elevations?

To check your answers, turn to page 111.

Subtracting Money

Gustavo bought a paperback book for $6.89. He paid the cashier with a $10 bill. How much change did he receive?

Remember to line up money problems with pennies under pennies, dimes under dimes, and dollars under dollars.

Example: $10 − $6.89 =

STEP 1.   Rewrite the problem. Notice that $10 goes left of the decimal point. Use zeros to hold the dimes and pennies places.

$$\begin{array}{r} \overset{9\ \ 9}{\cancel{10}\,\cancel{10}\,10} \\ \$1\cancel{0}.\cancel{0}\cancel{0} \\ -\ \ 6.89 \\ \hline \$3.11 \end{array}$$

STEP 2.   Regroup and subtract.

STEP 3.   Check $6.89 + $3.11 = $10.00.

⟯➤   Gustavo's change should be $3.11.

PRACTICE 14

Solve.

1. $20 − $12.89 = $8 − $2.56 = $10.50 − $10.33 =

2. $85 − $80.76 = $2.60 − $.99 = $9 − $8.17 =

3. $16.79 − $5 = $1.88 − $.36 = $50 − $32.79 =

4. $20 − $13.92 = $10.75 − $6.49 = $7 − $6.38 =

5. The Yoshimuras bought a gas grill. Including tax the price was $106.99. Mrs. Yoshimura paid $120 in cash. How much change did she receive?

6. In September an electric fan that originally sold for $39.49 was on sale for "$15 off." What was the sale price of the fan?

7. Sam paid a cashier $20 for lunch for Florene and himself. He received $4.36 in change. How much did the lunch cost?

8. John bought a baseball glove for $49.96 at Sports World. He later saw the same glove at another store for $54.98. How much did he save by buying the glove at Sports World?

To check your answers, turn to page 111.

Mixed Operations

Each of these problems takes more than one step to solve. Sometimes you will use both addition and subtraction. Read each problem carefully. You may want to write down the steps you must take to get the final answer.

PRACTICE 15

Solve.

1. For lunch Phil had a hamburger for $4.95, a cup of coffee for 85¢, and a piece of pie for $1.65. He paid with a $10 bill. How much change did he get?

2. Mrs. Romney works part time at the local drugstore. She earns $380 a week. From her check her employer deducts $28.30 for federal tax, $31.99 for Social Security, and $14.63 for state tax. What is her weekly net (take-home) pay?

3. Joe weighs 187 pounds. Jim weighs 174 pounds. They are loading a 645-pound washer/dryer onto an elevator. The limit that the elevator can safely carry is 1,500 pounds. With Joe, Jim, and the washer/dryer on the elevator, how much more weight could the elevator safely carry?

4. Mr. and Mrs. Rivera are driving 420 miles to visit their children. Before lunch they drive 192 miles. After lunch they drive 123 miles before they stop for coffee. How much farther do they have to drive to get to their children's house?

5. By May the Midvale Community Action Company hopes to raise $150,000. In March they had $49,520. In April they raised another $61,395. How much more money do they need?

6. Sam bought a tape deck that once sold for $399. It was on sale for "$75 off." By paying cash for the tape deck, Sam received an extra $15 discount. What was the final price Sam paid for the tape deck?

7. Deborah is on a diet of 2,500 calories a day. For breakfast she had 535 calories. For lunch she had 970 calories. How many calories can she have for the rest of the day?

8. The population of Central County is 427,342 people. The three largest towns are Midvale, Northton, and Easton. Midvale has a population of 126,387. Northton has a population of 93,568. Easton has a population of 68,591. How many people in Central County do not live in any of the three largest towns?

9. In September the Stroud family brought home $1,930.40. That month they spent $605 on mortgage payments, $549.78 for food, $97.53 for utilities, and $446.55 on other bills. How much did they have left after all their bills were paid?

The bar graph below shows the tax money that a Midwestern state collects in one year. Questions 10 through 14 refer to the graph.

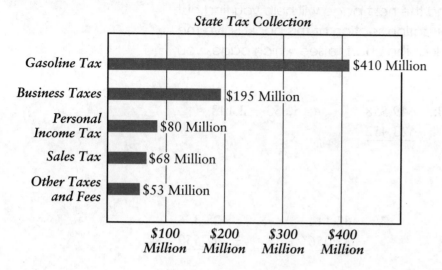

State Tax Collection

10. What is the total amount of tax that the state collects in one year?

11. The combined amount collected from personal income tax and sales tax is how much less than the amount collected from business taxes?

12. The yearly amount of gasoline tax is how much more than all the other sources of tax money put together?

13. What is the combined yearly amount collected from business taxes and personal income tax?

14. The amount collected annually from business taxes is how much less than the combined amount from personal income taxes, sales taxes, and other taxes and fees?

To check your answers, turn to page 112.

SUBTRACTION REVIEW

The problems on this page and the next page will help you find out if you need to review the subtraction section of this book. Solve the problems. When you finish, look at the chart to see which pages you should review.

1. $\begin{array}{r} 97 \\ -\ 34 \\ \hline \end{array}$

2. $\begin{array}{r} 826 \\ -\ 314 \\ \hline \end{array}$

3. $\begin{array}{r} 49{,}558 \\ -\ 23{,}452 \\ \hline \end{array}$

4. $5{,}653 - 2{,}143 =$

5. $\begin{array}{r} 264 \\ -\ 97 \\ \hline \end{array}$

6. $\begin{array}{r} 8{,}247 \\ -\ 3{,}548 \\ \hline \end{array}$

7. $\begin{array}{r} 62{,}114 \\ -\ 39{,}056 \\ \hline \end{array}$

8. $\begin{array}{r} 428{,}356 \\ -\ 297{,}559 \\ \hline \end{array}$

9. $862 - 379 =$

10. $4{,}281 - 3{,}196 =$

11. $24{,}228 - 9{,}369 =$

12. $316{,}253 - 97{,}188 =$

13. $\begin{array}{r} 600 \\ -\ 153 \\ \hline \end{array}$

14. $\begin{array}{r} 8{,}001 \\ -\ 2{,}446 \\ \hline \end{array}$

15. $\begin{array}{r} 30{,}000 \\ -\ 23{,}052 \\ \hline \end{array}$

16. $9{,}050 - 4{,}786 =$

17. Greg wants a jacket that sells for $159.95. It is on sale for $32.59 off the old price. Find the sale price.

18. The population of Smithville was 24,976 in 1970. The population was 43,328 in 1995. By how much did the population of Smithville increase from 1970 to 1995?

19. Deborah bought a new pair of shoes for $53.65. How much change did she get from $60?

20. A truck weighs 11,865 pounds when it is empty. It weighs 19,423 pounds when it is full. What is the weight of the load that was put into the truck?

PROGRESS CHECK

Check your answers on page 113. Then return to the review pages for the problems you missed. Correct your answers before going on to the next unit.

If you missed problems	*Review pages*
1 to 4	37 to 38
5 to 12 or 17, 18, or 20	39 to 42
13 to 16	43 to 47
19	48

Multiplication

Multiplication Facts

You could add to get multiplication answers, but it would be very slow. Multiplication is a fast method of adding. To multiply well, you must memorize the multiplication facts. Go through this exercise without adding. Check your answers. Then study the facts you missed until you can do this exercise with no errors.

PRACTICE 16

Solve.

1. 9	7	2	11	10	1	5	8
× 2	× 6	× 8	× 3	× 8	× 7	× 11	× 4

2. 3	10	8	5	3	10	1	6
× 3	× 11	× 8	× 4	× 5	× 6	× 9	× 3

3.
$$9 \times 0 \qquad 5 \times 7 \qquad 4 \times 9 \qquad 11 \times 8 \qquad 2 \times 12 \qquad 12 \times 7 \qquad 9 \times 3 \qquad 7 \times 2$$

4.
$$9 \times 12 \qquad 4 \times 1 \qquad 6 \times 6 \qquad 12 \times 10 \qquad 6 \times 0 \qquad 4 \times 7 \qquad 3 \times 12 \qquad 11 \times 5$$

5.
$$4 \times 4 \qquad 4 \times 6 \qquad 7 \times 3 \qquad 9 \times 8 \qquad 7 \times 10 \qquad 2 \times 2 \qquad 4 \times 11 \qquad 12 \times 8$$

6.
$$8 \times 2 \qquad 11 \times 10 \qquad 5 \times 12 \qquad 6 \times 8 \qquad 8 \times 12 \qquad 10 \times 1 \qquad 2 \times 11 \qquad 10 \times 3$$

7.
$$6 \times 9 \qquad 3 \times 7 \qquad 1 \times 2 \qquad 6 \times 2 \qquad 11 \times 7 \qquad 4 \times 12 \qquad 3 \times 2 \qquad 7 \times 0$$

8.
$$4 \times 2 \qquad 8 \times 6 \qquad 6 \times 12 \qquad 9 \times 9 \qquad 0 \times 5 \qquad 8 \times 11 \qquad 7 \times 9 \qquad 5 \times 2$$

9.
$$2 \times 1 \qquad 10 \times 5 \qquad 6 \times 11 \qquad 3 \times 9 \qquad 5 \times 1 \qquad 2 \times 4 \qquad 3 \times 4 \qquad 10 \times 2$$

10.
$$12 \times 1 \qquad 7 \times 8 \qquad 5 \times 9 \qquad 10 \times 10 \qquad 9 \times 7 \qquad 7 \times 5 \qquad 11 \times 6 \qquad 2 \times 9$$

11.

4	11	6	12	5	4	8	5
×10	× 4	× 7	× 4	×10	× 3	×10	× 5

12.

6	9	11	4	0	10	12	11
× 5	× 5	×11	× 8	×11	× 4	× 3	× 9

13.

3	12	9	8	12	9	5	12
× 0	×12	× 4	× 7	× 9	×10	× 3	× 5

14.

2	1	8	2	1	10	8	9
× 6	×10	× 9	× 3	× 1	× 7	× 0	×11

15.

5	12	6	0	9	3	7	8
× 8	× 6	× 4	× 8	× 6	×11	×12	× 3

16.

1	12	2	3	12	5	8	2
× 6	×11	× 5	× 8	× 4	× 6	× 5	×10

17.

11	7	10	2	3	0	7	1
× 2	× 7	×12	× 7	×10	×12	×11	× 3

18.

1	3	11	6	7	10	11	4
× 4	× 6	× 0	×10	× 4	× 9	×12	× 5

To check your answers, turn to page 113.

The Multiplication Table

The facts in the multiplication table are among the most important building blocks of mathematics. On this page is the multiplication table from 1 to 12. To find a multiplication fact, pick one number in the left-hand column. Then find the other number in the top row. From the left-hand number, follow across the row. From the top number, follow down the column. Where the row and column meet is the answer. For example, to find 8 times 6, find 8 at the left and 6 at the top of the table. Follow 8 across and 6 down until they meet. They meet at 48. $8 \times 6 = 48$.

	1	2	3	4	5	6	7	8	9	10	11	12
1	1	2	3	4	5	6	7	8	9	10	11	12
2	2	4	6	8	10	12	14	16	18	20	22	24
3	3	6	9	12	15	18	21	24	27	30	33	36
4	4	8	12	16	20	24	28	32	36	40	44	48
5	5	10	15	20	25	30	35	40	45	50	55	60
6	6	12	18	24	30	36	42	48	54	60	66	72
7	7	14	21	28	35	42	49	56	63	70	77	84
8	8	16	24	32	40	48	56	64	72	80	88	96
9	9	18	27	36	45	54	63	72	81	90	99	108
10	10	20	30	40	50	60	70	80	90	100	110	120
11	11	22	33	44	55	66	77	88	99	110	121	132
12	12	24	36	48	60	72	84	96	108	120	132	144

The table is meant to be used as a study tool, not as a crutch. Do not depend on this table to do problems in this book. Take the time to memorize the facts in the table. Do not try to memorize the entire table all at once. Memorize one column at a time. If you do, you will find the rest of the material in this book much easier.

Multiplication of Larger Numbers

To raise money, a volunteer fire department sold raffle tickets at $2 each. They sold 823 tickets. How much money did they raise?

The answer to a multiplication problem is called the **product.** To find the product of a large number and a one-digit number, begin at the right. Multiply every digit in the large number by the one-digit number.

Example: $823 \times 2 =$

STEP 1. $2 \times 3 = 6.$

STEP 2. $2 \times 2 = 4.$

STEP 3. $2 \times 8 = 16.$

$$\begin{array}{r} 823 \\ \times\ \ 2 \\ \hline 1,646 \end{array}$$

⟱➡ The firemen raised $1,646.

There is no easy way to check a multiplication problem. You can divide your answer by the bottom number in the problem. If you get the top number, your answer is correct. An easier method is to repeat the steps and watch for mistakes. It is a good idea in all mathematical problems to go over every step you have completed.

PRACTICE 17

Multiply and check.

1.
62	73	81	90	51	84	32
× 4	× 3	× 9	× 7	× 6	× 2	× 4

2.
53	80	74	42	91	60	71
× 3	× 8	× 2	× 3	× 7	× 5	× 8

3.
701	432	514	622	733	420
× 8	× 3	× 2	× 4	× 1	× 3

4.

911	621	713	842	304	621
× 7	× 2	× 3	× 2	× 2	× 4

5.

8,021	7,302	4,331	6,220	9,123
× 4	× 3	× 2	× 1	× 3

To check your answers, turn to page 114.

Multiplication by Two- and Three-Digit Numbers

Marvin works at a book bindery. What is the combined weight of 72 cartons of books if each carton weighs 43 pounds?

To multiply by a two-digit number, start with the digit in the ones place. Multiply each digit of the top number by the units of the bottom number. The first digit of this **partial product** should be directly under the units column. Then multiply each digit of the top number by the tens digit in the bottom number. The first digit of this partial product should be directly under the tens column. Continue until you have a partial product for each digit in the bottom number. Add the partial products to get the final product.

Example: $72 \times 43 =$

STEP 1. $3 \times 2 = 6$

STEP 2. $3 \times 7 = 21$
216 is the first partial product.

$$\begin{array}{r} 72 \\ \times\ 43 \\ \hline 216 \end{array}$$

STEP 3. $4 \times 2 = 8$

STEP 4. $4 \times 7 = 28$
288 is the second partial product.

$$\begin{array}{r} 72 \\ \times\ 43 \\ \hline 216 \\ 2\,88 \\ \hline 3{,}096 \end{array}$$

STEP 5.   Add the partial products.

➠   The combined weight of the cartons is 3,096 pounds.

PRACTICE 18

A. Multiply and check.

1.
$$\begin{array}{r}71\\ \times\,64\\\hline\end{array}\qquad\begin{array}{r}42\\ \times\,31\\\hline\end{array}\qquad\begin{array}{r}83\\ \times\,22\\\hline\end{array}\qquad\begin{array}{r}54\\ \times\,12\\\hline\end{array}\qquad\begin{array}{r}92\\ \times\,34\\\hline\end{array}\qquad\begin{array}{r}61\\ \times\,87\\\hline\end{array}\qquad\begin{array}{r}33\\ \times\,21\\\hline\end{array}$$

2.
$$\begin{array}{r}91\\ \times\,87\\\hline\end{array}\qquad\begin{array}{r}63\\ \times\,23\\\hline\end{array}\qquad\begin{array}{r}50\\ \times\,47\\\hline\end{array}\qquad\begin{array}{r}72\\ \times\,31\\\hline\end{array}\qquad\begin{array}{r}81\\ \times\,56\\\hline\end{array}\qquad\begin{array}{r}43\\ \times\,32\\\hline\end{array}\qquad\begin{array}{r}84\\ \times\,12\\\hline\end{array}$$

3.
$$\begin{array}{r}312\\ \times\,24\\\hline\end{array}\qquad\begin{array}{r}502\\ \times\,33\\\hline\end{array}\qquad\begin{array}{r}731\\ \times\,22\\\hline\end{array}\qquad\begin{array}{r}604\\ \times\,12\\\hline\end{array}\qquad\begin{array}{r}330\\ \times\,13\\\hline\end{array}\qquad\begin{array}{r}413\\ \times\,32\\\hline\end{array}$$

When you multiply by a three-digit number, the first digit of the last partial product should begin under the hundreds.

Example: Multiply 312 by 231.

$$\begin{array}{r}312\\ \times\,231\\\hline 312\\ 9\,36\\ 62\,4\\\hline 72{,}072\end{array}$$

B. Multiply and check.

4.
$$\begin{array}{r}240\\ \times\,122\\\hline\end{array}\qquad\begin{array}{r}521\\ \times\,331\\\hline\end{array}\qquad\begin{array}{r}602\\ \times\,243\\\hline\end{array}\qquad\begin{array}{r}731\\ \times\,223\\\hline\end{array}\qquad\begin{array}{r}523\\ \times\,113\\\hline\end{array}\qquad\begin{array}{r}324\\ \times\,212\\\hline\end{array}$$

5.
$$\begin{array}{r}511\\ \times\,781\\\hline\end{array}\qquad\begin{array}{r}632\\ \times\,314\\\hline\end{array}\qquad\begin{array}{r}313\\ \times\,221\\\hline\end{array}\qquad\begin{array}{r}421\\ \times\,423\\\hline\end{array}\qquad\begin{array}{r}305\\ \times\,111\\\hline\end{array}\qquad\begin{array}{r}732\\ \times\,231\\\hline\end{array}$$

6.

6,211	5,032	9,220	8,132	7,203
× 433	× 312	× 241	× 311	× 323

7.

4,078	4,132	6,110	7,120	2,321
× 111	× 332	× 785	× 224	× 123

8.

9,122	6,203	3,340	8,012	2,403
× 344	× 223	× 212	× 143	× 213

To check your answers, turn to page 114.

Multiplication with Carrying

Imani makes $9 an hour. How much did she make in a week when she worked 38 hours?

When you multiply two digits, the product is often a two-digit number. You must **carry** the left digit to the next number you are multiplying. Add the digit you carry to the next product.

Example: 38 × 9 =

STEP 1. 9 × 8 = 72. Write 2 under the units column and carry 7 to the tens column.

$$\begin{array}{r} 7 \\ 38 \\ \times\ 9 \\ \hline 342 \end{array}$$

STEP 2. 9 × 3 = 27. Add the 7 you carried. 27 + 7 = 34.

$$\begin{array}{r} 7 \\ 38 \\ \times\ 9 \\ \hline 342 \end{array}$$

⟹ Imani made $342 that week.

PRACTICE 19

A. Multiply and check.

1.
$$\begin{array}{r} 76 \\ \times\ 3 \\ \hline \end{array}$$
$$\begin{array}{r} 14 \\ \times\ 6 \\ \hline \end{array}$$
$$\begin{array}{r} 57 \\ \times\ 4 \\ \hline \end{array}$$
$$\begin{array}{r} 49 \\ \times\ 9 \\ \hline \end{array}$$
$$\begin{array}{r} 36 \\ \times\ 7 \\ \hline \end{array}$$
$$\begin{array}{r} 48 \\ \times\ 8 \\ \hline \end{array}$$
$$\begin{array}{r} 54 \\ \times\ 5 \\ \hline \end{array}$$

2.
$$\begin{array}{r} 29 \\ \times\ 6 \\ \hline \end{array}$$
$$\begin{array}{r} 65 \\ \times\ 9 \\ \hline \end{array}$$
$$\begin{array}{r} 78 \\ \times\ 2 \\ \hline \end{array}$$
$$\begin{array}{r} 53 \\ \times\ 9 \\ \hline \end{array}$$
$$\begin{array}{r} 68 \\ \times\ 4 \\ \hline \end{array}$$
$$\begin{array}{r} 84 \\ \times\ 7 \\ \hline \end{array}$$
$$\begin{array}{r} 38 \\ \times\ 3 \\ \hline \end{array}$$

3.
$$\begin{array}{r} 47 \\ \times\ 8 \\ \hline \end{array}$$
$$\begin{array}{r} 77 \\ \times\ 5 \\ \hline \end{array}$$
$$\begin{array}{r} 19 \\ \times\ 2 \\ \hline \end{array}$$
$$\begin{array}{r} 73 \\ \times\ 6 \\ \hline \end{array}$$
$$\begin{array}{r} 44 \\ \times\ 9 \\ \hline \end{array}$$
$$\begin{array}{r} 96 \\ \times\ 7 \\ \hline \end{array}$$
$$\begin{array}{r} 56 \\ \times\ 4 \\ \hline \end{array}$$

4.
$$\begin{array}{r} 27 \\ \times\ 5 \\ \hline \end{array}$$
$$\begin{array}{r} 82 \\ \times\ 8 \\ \hline \end{array}$$
$$\begin{array}{r} 53 \\ \times\ 6 \\ \hline \end{array}$$
$$\begin{array}{r} 39 \\ \times\ 7 \\ \hline \end{array}$$
$$\begin{array}{r} 88 \\ \times\ 4 \\ \hline \end{array}$$
$$\begin{array}{r} 72 \\ \times\ 9 \\ \hline \end{array}$$
$$\begin{array}{r} 35 \\ \times\ 3 \\ \hline \end{array}$$

Rewrite each problem. Put the number with fewer digits on the bottom. Then multiply and check.

5. $6 \times 92 =$ $73 \times 7 =$ $4 \times 89 =$ $76 \times 8 =$ $7 \times 68 =$

6. $47 \times 5 =$ $3 \times 68 =$ $72 \times 7 =$ $4 \times 93 =$ $66 \times 9 =$

7.
$$\begin{array}{r} 338 \\ \times\ 6 \\ \hline \end{array}$$
$$\begin{array}{r} 146 \\ \times\ 3 \\ \hline \end{array}$$
$$\begin{array}{r} 347 \\ \times\ 9 \\ \hline \end{array}$$
$$\begin{array}{r} 696 \\ \times\ 4 \\ \hline \end{array}$$
$$\begin{array}{r} 854 \\ \times\ 5 \\ \hline \end{array}$$
$$\begin{array}{r} 556 \\ \times\ 7 \\ \hline \end{array}$$

8.
$$\begin{array}{r} 809 \\ \times\ 7 \\ \hline \end{array}$$
$$\begin{array}{r} 706 \\ \times\ 9 \\ \hline \end{array}$$
$$\begin{array}{r} 407 \\ \times\ 8 \\ \hline \end{array}$$
$$\begin{array}{r} 503 \\ \times\ 4 \\ \hline \end{array}$$
$$\begin{array}{r} 209 \\ \times\ 5 \\ \hline \end{array}$$
$$\begin{array}{r} 608 \\ \times\ 6 \\ \hline \end{array}$$

Whole Numbers

9.   580   860   340   720   190   670
   × 7   × 8   × 6   × 5   × 9   × 4

10. 4,827   5,736   5,543   9,248   2,793
   ×   3   ×   4   ×   7   ×   6   ×   8

11.   68   17   32   74   54   95   24
    × 46   × 22   × 29   × 65   × 52   × 57   × 98

12. 548   372   276   179   788   854
   × 35   × 96   × 27   × 83   × 54   × 26

13. 962   339   528   447   235   463
   × 47   × 62   × 45   × 28   × 56   × 78

14. 704   516   428   903   728   637
   × 19   × 62   × 43   × 25   × 61   × 84

Zero multiplied by any number is 0. When multiplying by zero, you can save time by putting a single 0 in the column where the multiplying begins. Compare these two examples.

Acceptable Method: 27
                        × 30
                        ‾‾‾‾
                          00
                          81
                        ‾‾‾‾
                         810

Better Method: 27
                        × 30
                        ‾‾‾‾
                         810

B. Multiply and check.

15.
$$\begin{array}{r} 82 \\ \times\ 60 \\ \hline \end{array}$$
$$\begin{array}{r} 23 \\ \times\ 40 \\ \hline \end{array}$$
$$\begin{array}{r} 37 \\ \times\ 30 \\ \hline \end{array}$$
$$\begin{array}{r} 74 \\ \times\ 70 \\ \hline \end{array}$$
$$\begin{array}{r} 29 \\ \times\ 20 \\ \hline \end{array}$$

16.
$$\begin{array}{r} 43 \\ \times\ 70 \\ \hline \end{array}$$
$$\begin{array}{r} 97 \\ \times\ 40 \\ \hline \end{array}$$
$$\begin{array}{r} 65 \\ \times\ 60 \\ \hline \end{array}$$
$$\begin{array}{r} 46 \\ \times\ 30 \\ \hline \end{array}$$
$$\begin{array}{r} 38 \\ \times\ 50 \\ \hline \end{array}$$

17.
$$\begin{array}{r} 86 \\ \times\ 30 \\ \hline \end{array}$$
$$\begin{array}{r} 79 \\ \times\ 40 \\ \hline \end{array}$$
$$\begin{array}{r} 22 \\ \times\ 50 \\ \hline \end{array}$$
$$\begin{array}{r} 55 \\ \times\ 80 \\ \hline \end{array}$$
$$\begin{array}{r} 46 \\ \times\ 70 \\ \hline \end{array}$$

18.
$$\begin{array}{r} 942 \\ \times\ 750 \\ \hline 47\ 100 \\ 659\ 4 \\ \hline 706{,}500 \end{array}$$
$$\begin{array}{r} 604 \\ \times\ 803 \\ \hline \end{array}$$
$$\begin{array}{r} 203 \\ \times\ 560 \\ \hline \end{array}$$
$$\begin{array}{r} 735 \\ \times\ 290 \\ \hline \end{array}$$
$$\begin{array}{r} 596 \\ \times\ 804 \\ \hline \end{array}$$

Rewrite, multiply, and check.

19. $68 \times 509 =$ $681 \times 27 =$ $36 \times 725 =$

20. $858 \times 43 =$ $24 \times 679 =$ $915 \times 86 =$

21. $4{,}740 \times 26 =$ $37 \times 5{,}916 =$ $9{,}178 \times 72 =$

Solve the following.

22. Every row of the Midtown Theatre has 38 seats. There are 27 rows in the theatre. How many tickets does the manager have to sell to fill every seat?

23. Nate earns $14 an hour. How much does he earn working 35 hours a week?

24. Adrienne earns $24 an hour for overtime work. During her last pay period she worked 9 hours overtime. How much did she earn for overtime work that period?

25. Cecilia can type 82 words per minute. How many words can she type in 13 minutes?

26. There are three feet in one yard. Find the length in feet of a field that is 28 yards long.

27. A case of canned tomatoes holds 24 cans. How many cans are there in 30 cases?

28. There are 16 ounces in one pound. How many ounces are there in 18 pounds?

29. Ubaldo is paying back his student loan. He pays $132 a month for 24 months. Find the amount he is paying back.

30. For every CD that he sells in his shop, Mr. Johnson makes a profit of $2. Last month he sold 2,150 CDs. How much profit did he make from CDs last month?

To check your answers, turn to page 114.

Multiplication by 10, 100, and 1,000

Alan works on an assembly line. He can make 37 molded containers in one hour. How many containers can he make in 10 hours?

You have already learned a shortcut for multiplying numbers by zero. Multiplying by 10, 100, and 1,000 is even easier.

To multiply a number by 10, put a zero to the right of the number.

To multiply a number by 100, put two zeros to the right of the number.

To multiply a number by 1,000, put three zeros to the right of the number.

Examples: $10 \times 37 = 370$
$100 \times 52 = 5,200$
$1,000 \times 148 = 148,000$

➠   Alan can make 370 containers in 10 hours.

PRACTICE 20

Multiply and check.

1. $10 \times 82 =$ $10 \times 27 =$ $10 \times 68 =$ $10 \times 59 =$

2. $10 \times 528 =$ $10 \times 636 =$ $10 \times 798 =$ $10 \times 432 =$

3. $10 \times 929 =$ $541 \times 10 =$ $236 \times 10 =$ $10 \times 572 =$

4. $10 \times 360 =$ $450 \times 10 =$ $10 \times 720 =$ $990 \times 10 =$

5. $100 \times 39 =$ $100 \times 76 =$ $100 \times 52 =$ $100 \times 47 =$

6. $100 \times 634 =$ $100 \times 787 =$ $100 \times 512 =$ $100 \times 656 =$

7. $230 \times 100 =$ $470 \times 100 =$ $906 \times 100 =$ $405 \times 100 =$

8. $100 \times 20 =$ $30 \times 100 =$ $90 \times 100 =$ $100 \times 70 =$

9. $1{,}000 \times 8 =$ $1{,}000 \times 17 =$ $1{,}000 \times 26 =$ $1{,}000 \times 5 =$

10. $1{,}000 \times 30 =$ $50 \times 1{,}000 =$ $1{,}000 \times 40 =$ $20 \times 1{,}000 =$

11. $1{,}000 \times 387 =$ $1{,}000 \times 634 =$ $1{,}000 \times 911 =$ $1{,}000 \times 286 =$

12. One carton of books weighs 53 pounds. How much do 100 cartons of the same books weigh?

13. There are 4 quarts in a gallon. How many quarts are there in 10 gallons?

14. There are 5,280 feet in one mile. How many feet are there in 100 miles?

15. The Tree Huggers Association hopes to get $25 contributions from everyone they call. If they are successful, how much money can they raise from 1,000 donors?

16. The price for educating one child in the Midvale school system is $8,976. How much does it cost to educate 100 children?

17. Sulima is working at a food festival cooking dishes from her home country. If she makes an average of $195 a day, how much can she make in 10 days?

To check your answers, turn to page 115.

Estimation

Simon knows that he can drive about 28 miles on one gallon of gas. His gas tank holds 12 gallons. Estimate how far he can drive with a full tank of gas.

To **estimate** means to get an answer that is close but not exact. Round numbers to the nearest tens, hundreds, or thousands to estimate answers.

To review rounding, turn to page 14.

Example: Estimate 28 × 12.

STEP 1.   28 to the nearest ten is 30, and 12 to the nearest ten is 10.

STEP 2.   Carry out the operation with the rounded numbers.   30 × 10 = 300

⟹   Simon can drive about 300 miles on a full tank of gas.

The exact answer is 336 miles (28 × 12 = 336). The estimated answer is close to the exact answer.

PRACTICE 21

For each situation below use the hints to estimate answers.

There are 5,280 feet in a mile. The distance from Elena's house to the store where she works is about nine miles. Estimate the distance in feet.

1. Estimate with the number of feet in a mile rounded to the nearest thousand.

2. Estimate with the number of feet in a mile rounded to the nearest hundred and the number of miles rounded to the nearest ten.

3. Find the exact answer.

The Community Players sold 213 tickets for their Saturday night performance at $12 each. Estimate the amount they collected.

4. Estimate with ticket sales rounded to the nearest hundred.

5. Estimate with ticket sales rounded to the nearest hundred and ticket price rounded to the nearest ten.

6. Find the exact answer.

The total distance around a baseball diamond is 360 feet. In his career Mickey Mantle hit a total of 536 home runs. Estimate the total distance he ran to complete those home runs.

7. Estimate with the total number of home runs rounded to the nearest hundred.

8. Estimate with both numbers rounded to the nearest hundred.

9. Find the exact answer.

To check your answers, turn to page 115.

Using Formulas

A formula is a mathematical instruction. The distance formula $D = R \times T$ means "distance equals rate times time."

> D is *distance*, usually measured in miles.
> R is *rate*, usually measured in miles per hour.
> T is *time*, usually measured in hours.

Example: Michalis bicycles at a rate of 15 mph for 2 hours. How far does he travel?

STEP 1.   Replace R with 15 mph and T with
2 hours in the formula
$D = R \times T$.

$D = R \times T$
$D = 15 \times 2$
$D = 30$ miles

STEP 2.   Multiply 15×2.

➠   Michalis travels 30 miles.

PRACTICE 22

A. Use the distance formula to answer questions 1 to 5.

1. A plane travels at an average speed of 429 miles per hour. How far can the plane travel at this rate in four hours?

2. On the open road Jake drives at an average speed of 62 mph. How far can he travel in five hours?

3. How far does a train go in three hours at an average speed of 89 mph?

4. On a race track, a driver drives 6 hours at an average speed of 74 miles per hour. How many miles does the car travel?

5. Sandra hikes for 5 hours at an average speed of 4 miles per hour. How many miles does she hike?

The cost formula $C = N \times R$ means "cost equals the number of items or units times the rate."

C is *cost*, usually measured in dollars.
N is the *number* of items or units.
R is the *rate*, measured in units such as ¢ per pound or $ per yard.

Example: What is the cost of 3 yards of pressure-treated lumber at a rate of $2.40 a yard?

STEP 1.   Replace N with 3 and R with $2.40 $C = N \times R$
in the formula $C = N \times R$. $C = 3 \times \$2.40$
                                                $C = \$7.20$

STEP 2.   Multiply 3 × $2.40.

⟹   The lumber costs $7.20.

Remember in money problems to show the dimes and pennies places.

B. Use the cost formula to answer questions 6 to 9.

6. How much do five pounds of round roast cost if one pound costs $5.39?

7. Find the cost of seven gallons of paint if one gallon costs $14.99.

8. What is the price of three tubes of caulk if one tube costs $4.68?

9. Fill in the totals in the following lumber yard bill.

To check your answers, turn to page 116.

Item	Rate	Cost
20 feet of cedar siding	$1.40 per foot	_____
12 feet of 1-inch white pine	$1.12 per foot	_____
9 feet of 2-inch clear pine	$1.65 per foot	_____
TOTAL		_____

Mixed Operations

In some of these problems you will use more than one operation to find the solution. You may have to add, subtract, or multiply. Sometimes you will have to get information from a graph. Read each problem carefully.

PRACTICE 23

Solve.

1. There are 267 employees at the Consolidated Company. Every employee works 40 hours a week. The average hourly wage for an employee is $12. Based on the average wage, what is the total amount that the employees of Consolidated earn in one week?

2. There are nine buildings in the Hightower Project. Every building has twelve floors of apartments. Every floor houses six families. Each family has an average of four members. Find the total number of people living in the Hightower Project.

3. Melvin shipped 15 packages weighing 27 pounds each and 12 packages weighing 33 pounds each. What was the total weight of the shipment?

4. On Friday 283 people went to the George Street School Festival. On Saturday 365 people went to the festival. On Sunday, there were 344 people. Everyone paid $5 for a ticket. What was the total amount of the ticket sales for the festival?

5. The George Street Block Association hopes to raise $2,500 to renovate a playground. So far 56 families have given an average of $37 each. How much more does the Association need to raise?

The line graph below shows the approximate population of the United States from 1800 to 1990. Questions 6 through 10 are about this graph.

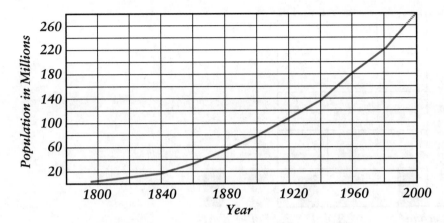

To find the population of the United States in a certain year, multiply the number on the graph by 1,000,000.

6. Find the population of the United States in these years:

   1800 _____   1860 _____   1920 _____   1960 _____

   1820 _____   1880 _____   1940 _____   1980 _____

7. How many more people lived in the U.S. in 1880 than in 1800?

8. If you multiply the U.S. population of 1820 by 5, the number you get is equal to the population in what year?

9. By how much did the population of the U.S. increase from 1880 to 1980?

10. In 1980 the average income for every person in the U.S. was $9,900. Find the income for the whole population in 1980.

The bar graph below shows the number of workers in each of the three shifts at the Midvale Manufacturing Company. Questions 11 through 15 are about this graph.

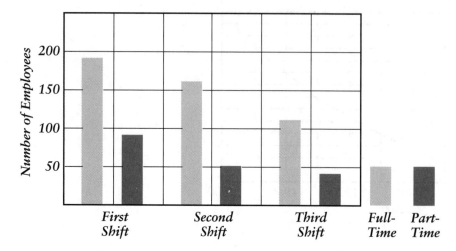

11. Tell how many full- and part-time workers are employed during each shift.

First Shift

full-time _____

part-time _____

Second Shift

full-time _____

part-time _____

Third Shift

full-time _____

part-time _____

12. What is the total number of full-time workers at the Midvale Manufacturing Company?

13. What is the total number of part-time workers at the Midvale Manufacturing Company?

14. Every employee at the Midvale Manufacturing Company works 40 hours a week. The average full-time employee earns $15 an hour. What is the total amount full-time employees earn there in one week?

15. Part-time workers work 30 hours per week. The average part-time wage is $13 an hour. What is the total amount that part-time employees earn there in one week?

To check your answers, turn to page 116.

MULTIPLICATION REVIEW

These problems will help you find out if you need to review the multiplication section of this book. Solve the problems. When you have finished, look at the chart to see which pages you should review.

1. 624
    × 2

2. 82
    × 34

3. 521
    × 41

4. 8,103
    × 223

5. 95
    × 7

6. 806
    × 9

7. 84
    × 56

8. 327
    × 60

9. 563
    × 87

10. 4,253
    × 46

11. 8 × 539 =

12. 486 × 29 =

13. 36 × 764 =

14. 285 × 2,067 =

15. 10 × 4,900 =

16. 1,285 × 1000 =

17. Eleven buses are going to Las Vegas. Each bus holds 42 people. Estimate the number of passengers who can travel on the buses by rounding both numbers to the nearest ten.

18. Omar has 6 storage containers. Each container holds about 215 VHS tapes. Estimate the number of tapes the containers can hold altogether by rounding the number of tapes to the nearest hundred.

19. A case holds 24 cans of soup. How many cans are there in 56 cases?

20. Janet earns $11 an hour. How much does she earn in 42 hours?

21. Michael is making 36 equal automobile payments. Each time he pays $130. What is the total amount of his automobile payments?

22. Ethel types 93 words per minute. How many words can she type in 30 minutes?

23. Karlene drives for 4 hours at an average speed of 25 miles per hour on a mountain road. Using the formula, $D = R \times T$, how many miles does she drive?

24. Marcus wants to buy 3 pounds of ground beef. At his butcher's shop, the meat sells for $2.87 per pound. Using the formula, $C = N \times R$, what is the cost of the ground beef?

PROGRESS CHECK

Check your answers on page 117. Then return to the review pages for the problems you missed. Correct your answers before going on to the next unit.

If you missed problems	Review pages
1 to 4	58 to 61
5 to 14, 19 to 22	61 to 65
15 to 16	66 to 67
17 to 18	68 to 69
23 to 24	70 to 71

Division

Division Facts

The division facts are the opposite of the multiplication facts. If you know the multiplication facts, you should have no trouble with this exercise. Do this exercise without help. Check your answers. Then study the facts you missed until you can do this exercise with no errors.

PRACTICE 24

Solve.

1. $6\overline{)42}$ $1\overline{)4}$ $3\overline{)27}$ $2\overline{)16}$ $3\overline{)24}$ $5\overline{)5}$ $2\overline{)14}$

2. $4\overline{)16}$ $8\overline{)56}$ $5\overline{)20}$ $9\overline{)81}$ $1\overline{)6}$ $8\overline{)48}$ $9\overline{)72}$

3. $2\overline{)8}$ $6\overline{)6}$ $4\overline{)24}$ $8\overline{)16}$ $6\overline{)54}$ $8\overline{)64}$ $4\overline{)12}$

4. $4\overline{)36}$ $7\overline{)7}$ $5\overline{)25}$ $2\overline{)2}$ $3\overline{)18}$ $6\overline{)24}$ $7\overline{)14}$

5. $6\overline{)48}$ $4\overline{)4}$ $5\overline{)30}$ $7\overline{)42}$ $3\overline{)3}$ $5\overline{)40}$ $4\overline{)28}$

6. $7\overline{)49}$ $6\overline{)36}$ $1\overline{)7}$ $5\overline{)15}$ $8\overline{)32}$ $7\overline{)56}$ $6\overline{)12}$

7. $7\overline{)35}$ $2\overline{)10}$ $4\overline{)8}$ $9\overline{)45}$ $3\overline{)15}$ $1\overline{)2}$ $4\overline{)32}$

8. $5\overline{)45}$ $2\overline{)12}$ $7\overline{)21}$ $3\overline{)21}$ $2\overline{)18}$ $8\overline{)72}$ $1\overline{)1}$

9. $9\overline{)27}$ $5\overline{)10}$ $7\overline{)63}$ $2\overline{)4}$ $4\overline{)20}$ $7\overline{)28}$ $6\overline{)18}$

10. $3\overline{)12}$ $9\overline{)54}$ $8\overline{)24}$ $1\overline{)9}$ $8\overline{)40}$ $9\overline{)18}$ $5\overline{)35}$

11. $2\overline{)6}$ $6\overline{)30}$ $9\overline{)36}$ $9\overline{)63}$ $3\overline{)9}$ $3\overline{)6}$ $1\overline{)8}$

To check your answers, turn to page 117.

Division by One Digit

Juanita's son Ben works at the neighborhood grocery store after school. He makes $7 an hour. One month he made $392. How many hours did he work?

The answer to a division problem is called the **quotient**. To find a quotient, repeat the four steps listed below until you complete the problem.

1. Divide.

2. Multiply.

3. Subtract and compare.

4. Bring down the next number.

Example: Divide 7 into 392.

STEP 1. **Divide:** $39 \div 7 = 5$. Write 5 above the tens place. Notice that 6 is too large and 4 is too small for the first step. $6 \times 7 = 42$, which is more than 39. $4 \times 7 = 28$, but $5 \times 7 = 35$, which is closer to 39.

$$\begin{array}{r} 5 \\ 7\overline{)392} \end{array}$$

STEP 2. **Multiply:** $5 \times 7 = 35$. Write 35 under 39.

$$\begin{array}{r} 5 \\ 7\overline{)392} \\ 35 \end{array}$$

STEP 3. **Subtract:** $39 - 35 = 4$. **Compare** to be sure that what you get by subtracting is less than what you are dividing by. 4 is less than 7.

$$\begin{array}{r} 5 \\ 7\overline{)392} \\ \underline{35} \\ 4 \end{array}$$

STEP 4. **Bring down the next number:** 2.

$$\begin{array}{r} 5 \\ 7\overline{)392} \\ \underline{35} \\ 42 \end{array}$$

STEP 5. **Divide:** $42 \div 7 = 6$. Write 6 above the units place.

$$\begin{array}{r} 56 \\ 7\overline{)392} \\ \underline{35} \\ 42 \end{array}$$

STEP 6. **Multiply:** $6 \times 7 = 42$. Write 42 under 42.

$$\begin{array}{r} 56 \\ 7\overline{)392} \\ \underline{35} \\ 42 \\ 42 \end{array}$$

STEP 7. **Subtract:** $42 - 42 = 0$. **Compare:** 0 is less than 7.

$$\begin{array}{r} 56 \\ 7\overline{)392} \\ \underline{35} \\ 42 \\ \underline{42} \\ 0 \end{array}$$

STEP 8. **Check:** $7 \times 56 = 392$.

➡ Ben worked 56 hours that month.

Writing every step, as the example shows in step 7, is called **long division**. In **short division** you write only the answer and the number you get by subtracting.

Example:
$$7)\overline{39^42}\ \ 5\ 6$$

Both long division and short division are all right when you divide by one digit.

To check a division problem, multiply your answer (the quotient) by the number you divided by. The product should equal the number you divided.

Example: $7)\overline{392}\ \ 56$ *Check:*

$$\begin{array}{r} 56 \\ \times\ \ 7 \\ \hline 392 \end{array}$$

PRACTICE 25

A. Divide and check.

1. $9)\overline{432}$ $6)\overline{456}$ $7)\overline{651}$ $2)\overline{128}$ $3)\overline{216}$

2. $5)\overline{430}$ $8)\overline{376}$ $4)\overline{292}$ $6)\overline{270}$ $7)\overline{392}$

3. $2)\overline{196}$ $9)\overline{243}$ $5)\overline{380}$ $3)\overline{249}$ $7)\overline{413}$

4. $8)\overline{496}$ $3)\overline{282}$ $3)\overline{171}$ $6)\overline{408}$ $5)\overline{360}$

5. $7)\overline{2,184}$ $6)\overline{5,076}$ $9)\overline{2,943}$ $3)\overline{1,956}$

6. $4)\overline{3,724}$ $7)\overline{3,346}$ $5)\overline{2,645}$ $8)\overline{5,096}$

7. $6\overline{)1,578}$ $3\overline{)1,437}$ $4\overline{)1,544}$ $9\overline{)6,768}$

8. $7\overline{)2,688}$ $2\overline{)1,732}$ $8\overline{)4,656}$ $5\overline{)3,390}$

9. $5\overline{)28,365}$ $6\overline{)53,232}$ $7\overline{)17,192}$ $3\overline{)9,861}$

10. $8\overline{)40,112}$ $7\overline{)53,256}$ $4\overline{)36,128}$ $5\overline{)12,045}$

11. $2\overline{)16,092}$ $4\overline{)36,268}$ $7\overline{)23,149}$ $6\overline{)25,806}$

12. $2\overline{)18,306}$ $7\overline{)23,695}$ $9\overline{)33,102}$ $3\overline{)23,496}$

If a division problem is written with the ÷ sign, rewrite the problem using the $\overline{)}$ sign. Notice the placement of the numbers with these two signs.

Example: $1,537 \div 29 =$ *Change to:*

$$\begin{array}{r} 53 \\ 29\overline{)1,537} \\ \underline{1\ 45} \\ 87 \\ \underline{87} \\ 0 \end{array}$$

B. Divide and check.

13. $1,560 \div 4 =$ $2,112 \div 3 =$ $3,320 \div 4 =$ $4,056 \div 8 =$

14. $7,236 \div 9 =$ $5,760 \div 6 =$ $3,290 \div 7 =$ $1,740 \div 3 =$

15. $2,359 \div 7 =$ $8,586 \div 9 =$ $1,872 \div 4 =$ $1,976 \div 8 =$

Solve the following.

16. Linda's living room is 24 feet long. There are three feet in one yard. What is the length of the room in yards?

17. Four co-workers shared a $5,000 lottery prize equally. How much did each of them receive?

18. Rolando cut a copper pipe 108 inches long into 6 equal pieces. How long was each piece?

19. The Andersons paid $61,180 for a seven-acre parcel of land where they plan to build a house. What was the price per acre?

20. Stavros and his two brothers run a coffee shop. One month they made a profit of $7,926. If they share the profit equally, how much will each brother get?

21. Eight friends estimate that the expenses for a trip to Las Vegas will be $1,872. If the friends share the cost of the trip equally, how much will each friend pay?

22. Carrie worked part time for nine months last year as a teacher's assistant. Her total pay for the job was $7,560. How much did she earn per month?

To check your answers, turn to page 118.

Division with Remainders

How many bottles each holding 5 gallons of cider can Robert fill from a barrel of cider that holds 118 gallons?

If you do not get zero in the last subtraction step of a division problem, you will get a **remainder**.

Example: Divide 118 by 5.

STEP 1.   **Divide:** $11 \div 5 = 2$. Write 2 above the tens place.

$$\begin{array}{r} 2 \\ 5\overline{)118} \end{array}$$

STEP 2.   **Multiply:** $2 \times 5 = 10$. Write 10 under 11.

$$\begin{array}{r} 2 \\ 5\overline{)118} \\ 10 \end{array}$$

STEP 3.   **Subtract:** $11 - 10 = 1$.
Compare: 1 is less than 5.

$$\begin{array}{r} 2 \\ 5\overline{)118} \\ 10 \\ \hline 1 \end{array}$$

STEP 4.   **Bring down the next number:** 8.

$$\begin{array}{r} 2 \\ 5\overline{)118} \\ 10 \\ \hline 18 \end{array}$$

STEP 5.   **Divide:** $18 \div 5 = 3$. Write 3 above the ones place.

$$\begin{array}{r} 23 \\ 5\overline{)118} \\ 10 \\ \hline 18 \end{array}$$

STEP 6.   **Multiply:** $3 \times 5 = 15$. Write 15 under 18.

$$\begin{array}{r} 23 \\ 5\overline{)118} \\ 10 \\ \hline 18 \\ 15 \end{array}$$

STEP 7.   **Subtract:** $18 - 15 = 3$.

$$
\begin{array}{r}
23\text{r}3 \\
5\overline{)118} \\
\underline{10} \\
18 \\
\underline{15} \\
3
\end{array}
$$

The r3 in the answer means there is a remainder of 3.

⟶   Robert can fill 23 bottles. There will be 3 gallons of cider left over.

To check a division problem with a remainder, multiply the answer of your division by the number you divided by and add the remainder.

Example: $23\text{r}3$
$5\overline{)118}$

Check:
$$
\begin{array}{r}
23 \\
\times\ \ 5 \\
\hline
115 \\
+\ \ \ 3 \\
\hline
118
\end{array}
$$

PRACTICE 26

Divide and check.

1. $3\overline{)143}$ $\quad$ $6\overline{)518}$ $\quad$ $9\overline{)349}$ $\quad$ $7\overline{)346}$ $\quad$ $2\overline{)151}$

2. $8\overline{)718}$ $\quad$ $3\overline{)217}$ $\quad$ $7\overline{)690}$ $\quad$ $4\overline{)111}$ $\quad$ $6\overline{)239}$

3. $7\overline{)185}$ $\quad$ $9\overline{)437}$ $\quad$ $8\overline{)741}$ $\quad$ $5\overline{)368}$ $\quad$ $2\overline{)139}$

4. $3\overline{)212}$ $\quad$ $6\overline{)304}$ $\quad$ $4\overline{)282}$ $\quad$ $9\overline{)725}$ $\quad$ $7\overline{)426}$

5. $8\overline{)540}$ $\quad$ $4\overline{)378}$ $\quad$ $6\overline{)347}$ $\quad$ $5\overline{)237}$ $\quad$ $3\overline{)268}$

6. $7\overline{)2,901}$ $\quad$ $8\overline{)5,813}$ $\quad$ $7\overline{)1,880}$ $\quad$ $9\overline{)3,434}$

Rewrite each problem, divide and check.

7. $1{,}945 \div 2 =$ $4{,}373 \div 5 =$ $2{,}914 \div 8 =$ $3{,}687 \div 4 =$

8. $2{,}430 \div 4 =$ $3{,}485 \div 6 =$ $6{,}586 \div 7 =$ $3{,}947 \div 7 =$

9. $4{,}723 \div 8 =$ $2{,}042 \div 5 =$ $2{,}246 \div 7 =$ $6{,}339 \div 9 =$

10. $1{,}453 \div 4 =$ $6{,}387 \div 7 =$ $2{,}248 \div 3 =$ $3{,}771 \div 6 =$

Use the following information to answer questions 11 and 12.

In order to make shelves, Sally is sawing pieces each, three feet long, from a board that is 16 feet long.

11. How many shelves can she cut from the long board?

12. Assuming no waste, find the length of the remaining piece when Sally finishes cutting shelves.

Use the following information to answer questions 13 and 14.

Fred is a furniture maker. He uses 9 feet of trim board to complete a coffee table. He has a total of 120 feet of trim board in his shop.

13. How many coffee tables can Fred trim with his supply of trim board?

14. If he uses his supply of trim board for coffee tables, how much will be left?

To check your answers, turn to page 118.

Division by Larger Numbers

Chris made $1,656 for 72 hours of work. How much did he make an hour?

To divide by two-digit and three-digit numbers, you must **estimate** how many times one number divides into another number. When you estimate, you make a guess.

Example: Divide 1,656 by 72.

STEP 1.   **Estimate** how many times 72 divides into 165. To do this, ask yourself how many times 7 divides into 16. $16 \div 7 = 2$, plus a remainder. Write 2 above the 5.

$$\begin{array}{r} 2 \\ 72\overline{)1,656} \end{array}$$

STEP 2.   **Multiply:** $2 \times 72 = 144$. Write 144 under 165.

$$\begin{array}{r} 2 \\ 72\overline{)1,656} \\ 1\,44 \end{array}$$

STEP 3.   **Subtract:** $165 - 144 = 21$.
Compare: 21 is less than 72.

$$\begin{array}{r} 2 \\ 72\overline{)1,656} \\ 1\,44 \\ \hline 21 \end{array}$$

STEP 4.   **Bring down the next number:** 6.

$$\begin{array}{r} 2 \\ 72\overline{)1,656} \\ 1\,44 \\ \hline 216 \end{array}$$

STEP 5.   **Estimate** how many times 72 divides into 216. To do this, ask yourself how many times 7 divides into 21. $21 \div 7 = 3$. Write 3 above the 6.

$$\begin{array}{r} 23 \\ 72\overline{)1,656} \\ 1\,44 \\ \hline 216 \end{array}$$

STEP 6.   **Multiply:** $3 \times 72 = 216$. Write 216 under 216.

$$\begin{array}{r} 23 \\ 72\overline{)1,656} \\ 1\,44 \\ \hline 216 \\ 216 \end{array}$$

STEP 7.   Subtract: $216 - 216 = 0$.

$$
\begin{array}{r}
23 \\
72\overline{)1{,}656} \\
1\ 44 \\
\hline
216 \\
216 \\
\hline
0
\end{array}
$$

STEP 8.   Check: $23 \times 72 = 1{,}656$.

⇒   Chris makes \$23 an hour.

Often your first estimate will be wrong. Work with a pencil and a good eraser. Decide whether your estimate is too small or too large and try again.

PRACTICE 27

Divide and check.

1. $39\overline{)351}$ $\qquad$ $61\overline{)305}$ $\qquad$ $43\overline{)301}$ $\qquad$ $89\overline{)267}$

2. $58\overline{)252}$ $\qquad$ $97\overline{)709}$ $\qquad$ $63\overline{)330}$ $\qquad$ $56\overline{)348}$

3. $24\overline{)1{,}968}$ $\qquad$ $18\overline{)1{,}314}$ $\qquad$ $61\overline{)2{,}745}$ $\qquad$ $46\overline{)2{,}852}$

4. $72\overline{)4{,}032}$ $\qquad$ $79\overline{)1{,}896}$ $\qquad$ $19\overline{)1{,}349}$ $\qquad$ $85\overline{)5{,}440}$

5. $47\overline{)2{,}451}$ $\qquad$ $64\overline{)2{,}382}$ $\qquad$ $72\overline{)3{,}112}$ $\qquad$ $34\overline{)2{,}656}$

6. $40\overline{)2{,}100}$ $\qquad$ $90\overline{)3{,}730}$ $\qquad$ $70\overline{)1{,}835}$ $\qquad$ $30\overline{)1{,}873}$

7. $37\overline{)2{,}590}$ $\qquad$ $48\overline{)2{,}880}$ $\qquad$ $62\overline{)4{,}982}$ $\qquad$ $81\overline{)3{,}270}$

8. $73\overline{)35{,}624}$ $\qquad$ $85\overline{)46{,}410}$ $\qquad$ $38\overline{)9{,}386}$ $\qquad$ $94\overline{)34{,}592}$

9. $39\overline{)35,607}$ $75\overline{)62,850}$ $68\overline{)51,204}$ $21\overline{)13,902}$

10. $37\overline{)25,974}$ $66\overline{)20,328}$ $17\overline{)7,820}$ $53\overline{)39,220}$

11. $86\overline{)31,670}$ $52\overline{)34,814}$ $68\overline{)62,318}$ $76\overline{)26,766}$

12. $982\overline{)20,622}$ $157\overline{)11,932}$ $316\overline{)29,388}$ $878\overline{)29,852}$

13. $936\overline{)80,696}$ $635\overline{)22,525}$ $123\overline{)6,742}$ $194\overline{)13,824}$

14. $216\overline{)13,040}$ $665\overline{)20,010}$ $945\overline{)66,250}$ $422\overline{)38,180}$

Rewrite, divide, and check.

15. $138 \div 46 =$ $198 \div 22 =$ $462 \div 77 =$ $216 \div 27 =$

16. $286 \div 44 =$ $152 \div 28 =$ $378 \div 52 =$ $305 \div 71 =$

17. $4,050 \div 50 =$ $3,290 \div 70 =$ $3,780 \div 60 =$

18. $28,880 \div 74 =$ $24,491 \div 51 =$ $13,116 \div 26 =$

19. $1,956 \div 326 =$ $5,744 \div 718 =$ $3,556 \div 508 =$

20. $17,910 \div 398 =$ $37,062 \div 522 =$ $48,880 \div 940 =$

     Whole Numbers

21. $17{,}544 \div 204 =$ $27{,}784 \div 302 =$ $32{,}629 \div 487 =$

Solve the following.

22. How many five-pound bags of sugar can be filled from a barrel that holds 215 pounds of sugar?

23. Last year the Mejias paid a total of $6,516 for rent. What was their monthly rent? [**Hint:** Remember there are 12 months in a year.]

24. A case holds 24 bottles of cola. How many cases can be filled with 864 bottles of cola?

25. Tim drove 312 miles to visit his son, who is away at college. Normally Tim gets 26 miles per gallon of gasoline. How many gallons of gasoline did he use driving to visit his son?

26. Floria has agreed to pay $3,096 for furniture for her new apartment. She will make 43 equal monthly payments. How much will she pay each month?

27. There are 5,280 feet in one mile. What is the height in miles of a mountain that is 21,120 feet high?

28. Pete wants to save $1,645 to buy a motorcycle. He plans to save $35 from his paycheck each week. How many weeks will he need to save enough to buy the motorcycle?

29. An airplane travels at an average speed of 415 miles per hour. How many hours will it take the plane to fly 2,905 miles? [**Hint:** Divide the total miles by the average speed.]

To check your answers, turn to page 119.

Using Formulas

PRACTICE 28

Read the description of each formula. Then use the formula to solve the problems.

To find a driving rate or speed, use the formula $R = D \div T$. The formula means "rate equals distance traveled divided by time of travel."

A. Use the formula $R = D \div T$ to answer questions 1 to 3.

1. Maria drove 144 miles in three hours. What was her average driving speed?

2. A train traveled 276 miles in four hours. What was the average speed of the train?

3. On a bicycle trip, Georgios went 102 miles in six hours. What was his average speed that day?

To find travel time, use the formula $T = D \div R$. The formula means "time equals distance divided by rate or average speed."

B. Use the formula $T = D \div R$ to answer questions 4 and 5.

4. How long does it take a train to go 344 miles if it travels at an average speed of 86 miles per hour?

5. Sam is a truck driver. He has to drive to a city that is 1,265 miles away. He knows that he can maintain an average speed of 55 miles per hour. How many hours will Sam have to drive?

You have already seen the word *average* in this book. An average is a total divided by the number of items in the total. The formula for finding the average of two numbers is $(A + B) \div 2$ where A and B are the two numbers. The parentheses mean that you should add the two numbers first. Then divide the sum by 2.

C. Use the formula for the average of two numbers to answer questions 6 to 8.

6. On his first math test, Bill got a score of 77. On the second test, his score was 95. Find the average of his scores.

7. Sally works as a waitress part time. Friday her tips were $124.60, and Saturday her tips were $88.90. Find her average daily tips for those two days.

8. Phil does hauling for a construction company. One morning he took a load of demolition material that weighed 892 pounds. That afternoon he took another load that weighed 1,116 pounds. Find the average weight of the loads.

The formula for finding the average of three numbers is $(A + B + C) \div 3$ where A, B, and C are the three numbers.

D. Use the formula for the average of three numbers for solving problems 9 to 11.

9. In Minneapolis the average temperature in December is 20° Fahrenheit. The average temperature in January is 14°. The average temperature in February is 17°. What is the average temperature for that three-month period?

10. Mr. Johnson earned $29,600 last year. Mrs. Johnson earned $17,080. Their son Jamal earned $5,250. What was the average yearly income for each member of the Johnson family?

11. On Friday Carlos drove 784 miles from Dallas to Denver. On Saturday he drove 615 miles from Denver to Oklahoma City. On Sunday he drove 215 miles from Oklahoma City back to Dallas. What was the average distance that Carlos drove each day?

To find the price of an item when you know the price of several items and the number of items purchased, use the formula $R = C \div N$. R stands for unit rate which means the cost of one item. The formula means "unit rate equals the cost of several items divided by the number of items.

E. Use the formula $R = C \div N$ to answer questions 12 to 15.

12. Ron paid $132 for twelve 5-gallon cans of blacktop sealer. What was the price per can?

13. A teacher paid $192 for a classroom set of 32 calculators. What was the price per calculator?

14. A case of video cassettes costs $108. If the case contains 36 cassettes, what is the cost of one cassette?

15. On Friday, Software Discount sold 25 copies of Space Jockey, a new computer game. The store collected $1,200 for the software sold. What was the price of one copy of Space Jockey?

To check your answers, turn to page 119.

Mixed Operations

In some of the next problems, you will use more than one operation to find the solution. You may need to add, subtract, multiply, or divide. You may have to get information from a graph or a table. Read each problem carefully.

PRACTICE 29

Use the following information to answer questions 1 and 2.

> Mr. and Mrs. Tullio are buying carpet for their living room and dining room. The living room has an area of 216 square feet, and the dining room has an area of 108 square feet. The carpet they want costs $24 a square yard, and they must pay a delivery and installation charge of $150.

1. There are 9 square feet in a square yard. What is the area in square yards of the floor space that the Tullios want to have carpeted?

2. Including delivery and installation, what is the price of the carpet?

Use the following information to answer questions 3 and 4.

> Jeff and Manny started a business a year ago. Jeff invested $16,000, and Manny invested $14,500. By the end of the year, their business made $52,000. They agreed to split the earnings by first taking the amount each of them had originally invested. Then they divided the rest evenly.

3. How much money did Jeff get back from the business?

4. How much money did Manny get?

5. Kate bought a sofa that originally cost $498. It was on sale for $122 less. She agreed to pay for the sofa in four equal installments. How much is each payment?

Use the following information to answer questions 6 to 9.

Frank is a carpenter. He plans to build five bookcases. He paid $290 for lumber, $15 for screws, and $30 for varnish.

6. What was the cost of materials for one bookcase?

7. Frank charged $175 for each bookcase. How much money did he make on one bookcase?

8. How much did he make on all five bookcases?

9. Frank worked 30 hours to make the five bookcases. How much did he earn for each hour of his work?

The chart below shows the production of three different crops in the U.S. for one year. Use the chart to answer questions 10 to 15.

Crop	Yearly Production (bushels)	Yield per Acre (bushels)	Price per Bushel ($)
corn	7,854,000,000	119	$2
wheat	2,740,000,000	40	$3
soybeans	1,921,000,000	34	$6

How much is an average acre worth of:

10. corn? _____

To find how much a farmer can get from an average acre of a crop, multiply the price of one bushel by the yield per acre.

Whole Numbers

11. wheat? _____

12. soybeans? _____

How many acres of farmland in the U.S. were used to produce:

13. corn? _____

To find the number of acres used to produce each crop, divide the yearly production of each crop by the yield per acre.

14. wheat? _____

15. soybeans? _____

The graph below shows the yearly car sales of four different companies. Each picture stands for 500 cars. Use the chart to answer questions 16 to 20.

16. How many cars did each company sell?

To find the number of cars each company sold, multiply the number of pictures by 500.

Company A _____

Company B _____

Company C _____

Company D _____

17. Company A sold how many times as many cars as Company B?

18. The combined car sales of Companies B, C, and D is how much less than the sales of Company A?

19. Company C learned that one out of every 20 cars they sold had to be returned for major repairs. How many cars were returned to Company C for major repairs?

20. A company in another state, Company E, sold 3,500 cars in the same year. How many pictures are needed to show the car sales of Company E on the graph?

Use the following information to answer questions 21 to 24.

Midvale Elementary School is planning to install a new computer lab for its students. The lab will have 15 computer stations. The cost of the 15 computers will be $20,250. The cost of furniture for 1 station will be $295. Three corporate sponsors will donate equal shares to pay for the equipment and furnishings.

21. What is the cost of one computer?

22. How much will the furniture for 15 computer stations cost?

23. What is the total cost of the computers and furniture?

24. How much will each corporate sponsor donate?

To check your answers, turn to page 120.

DIVISION REVIEW

Here are some problems to find out if you need to review the division section of this book. Solve the problems. When you have finished, look at the chart to see which pages you should review.

1. $7\overline{)392}$ 2. $9\overline{)2,673}$ 3. $6\overline{)4,824}$ 4. $5\overline{)164}$ 5. $8\overline{)526}$

6. $4\overline{)2,838}$ 7. $32\overline{)256}$ 8. $51\overline{)2,193}$ 9. $79\overline{)4,197}$

10. $85\overline{)3,160}$ 11. $63\overline{)4,422}$ 12. $226\overline{)16,272}$ 13. $418\overline{)10,868}$

14. $945 \div 15 =$ 15. $648 \div 36 =$ 16. $2,268 \div 27 =$

17. Last year Lynne paid $5,400 for rent. There are 12 months in a year. How much rent did Lynne pay each month?

18. There are 36 inches in one yard. How many yards are there in 1,872 inches?

19. A train travels at an average speed of 48 miles per hour. How long will it take the train to travel 864 miles?

20. John is making a payment of $128 every month on his motorcycle. How many months will it take John to pay the $2,944 that he owes?

PROGRESS CHECK

Check your answers on page 121. Then return to the review pages for the problems you missed. Correct your answers before going on to the next unit.

If you missed problems	*Review pages*
1 to 3	77 to 82
4 to 6	83 to 85
7 to 20	86 to 92

These problems will tell you which sections of this book you need to review before going on to the next book in this series, *New Basic Skills with Math: Decimals.* When you have finished, check the chart to see which pages you need to review.

In problems 1 to 4 read the number. Then write out the missing words in the name of the number.

1. 90,250,000

   ninety _____, two hundred fifty _____.

2. 8,017,600

   eight _____, seventeen _____, six _____.

3. 4,300,019,000

   four _____, three hundred _____, nineteen

   _____.

4. 170,850,020

   one hundred seventy _____, eight hundred fifty

   _____, twenty.

In problems 5 to 8 read the numbers. Then write the numbers in figures.

5. two thousand forty   _____

6. eighteen thousand, nine hundred   _____

7. three million, six thousand, eight hundred   _____

8. fourteen million, two hundred seventy thousand _____

9. Round off 749 to the nearest hundred. _____

10. Round off 16,458 to the nearest ten thousand. _____

Solve.

11. $\begin{array}{r} 325 \\ + 263 \\ \hline \end{array}$ 12. $\begin{array}{r} 4,207 \\ + 3,582 \\ \hline \end{array}$ 13. $\begin{array}{r} 165,204 \\ + 331,590 \\ \hline \end{array}$ 14. 516 + 82 =

15. 293 + 104 = 16. 81,243 + 8,251 =

17. $\begin{array}{r} 47 \\ 93 \\ + 65 \\ \hline \end{array}$ 18. $\begin{array}{r} 418 \\ 96 \\ + 284 \\ \hline \end{array}$ 19. $\begin{array}{r} 4,180 \\ 51,285 \\ + 3,678 \\ \hline \end{array}$

20. $\begin{array}{r} 6,394 \\ 4,397 \\ + 2,552 \\ \hline \end{array}$ 21. $\begin{array}{r} 47,096 \\ 69,374 \\ + 93,215 \\ \hline \end{array}$ 22. $\begin{array}{r} 82,384 \\ 19,657 \\ + 42,155 \\ \hline \end{array}$

23. 57 + 546 + 1,656 = 24. 3,608 + 18 + 642 =

25. 14 + 936 + 2,985 = 26. 16 + 20,350 + 186 + 2,419 =

27. $\begin{array}{r} 87 \\ - 36 \\ \hline \end{array}$ 28. $\begin{array}{r} 453 \\ - 212 \\ \hline \end{array}$ 29. $\begin{array}{r} 38,279 \\ - 24,135 \\ \hline \end{array}$ 30. 7,925 − 1,312 =

31.   83
       − 37

32.   5,432
     − 2,885

33.   77,063
     − 48,156

34.   329,142
     − 189,466

35. 437 − 89 =

36. 240 − 153 =

37. 3,242 − 1,975 =

38. 38,362 − 18,593 =

39.   400
     − 193

40.   6,000
     − 2,546

41.   40,070
     − 23,564

42. 9,000 − 2,536 =

43.   824
      × 2

44.   53
      × 32

45.   822
      ×214

46.   4,302
      × 231

47.   87
      × 9

48.   470
      × 6

49.   56
      ×84

50.   376
      × 70

51.   297
      × 46

52.   3,472
      ×   78

53. 926 × 7 =

54. 39 × 877 =

55. 236 × 48 =

56. 345 × 2,907 =

57. 280 × 100 =

58. 1,000 × 470 =

59. $8\overline{)656}$ 60. $5\overline{)1,535}$ 61. $4\overline{)1,852}$ 62. $7\overline{)228}$ 63. $6\overline{)491}$

64. $9\overline{)3,891}$ 65. $81\overline{)729}$ 66. $22\overline{)792}$ 67. $63\overline{)1,794}$

68. $43\overline{)2,592}$ 69. $82\overline{)3,310}$ 70. $196\overline{)10,976}$ 71. $358\overline{)13,604}$

72. $3,282 \div 68 =$ 73. $1,392 \div 24 =$ 74. $3,599 \div 59 =$

75. Jill is a waitress. She estimated her tips for the week were: Monday, $24; Tuesday, $13; Wednesday, $18; Thursday, $30; and Friday, $35. About how much did she make in tips all together that week?

76. Mr. Hicks was born in 1898. How old was Mr. Hicks in 1995?

77. The distance from Midvale to Northton is 126 miles. Easton is 98 miles beyond Northton. Find the distance from Midvale to Easton by way of Northton.

78. Matt gets an average of 21 miles per gallon of gasoline. How many miles can he drive with 18 gallons of gasoline?

79. In a recent year the city government of New York spent an average of $4,256 for every citizen. The Washington, D.C., municipal government spent an average of $6,713. Find the difference between the amounts spent by New York and Washington on each citizen.

80. One pound contains 16 ounces. How many pounds are there in 1,088 ounces?

81. A box contains 48 bottles of ketchup. How many bottles are there in 27 boxes filled with ketchup bottles?

82. In one week the Central Storage Company received 252,342 pounds of furniture. It took 27 trucks to deliver the furniture. What was the average weight that each truck delivered?

83. One pound of lean ground beef costs $3. How much do seven pounds of lean ground beef cost?

84. Pete drives at an average speed of 53 miles per hour. How many hours will he need to drive 636 miles?

Check your answers on page 121. Circle the problems you missed on the chart below. Review the pages that show how to work the problems you missed. Then try the problems again.

Problem Number	Review Pages	Problem Number	Review Pages	Problem Number	Review Pages
1	9–11	29	37–39	57	66–67
2	9–11	30	37–39	58	66–67
3	9–11	31	39–42	59	78–82
4	9–11	32	39–42	60	78–82
5	11–13	33	39–42	61	78–82
6	11–13	34	39–42	62	83–85
7	11–13	35	39–42	63	83–85
8	11–13	36	39–42	64	83–85
9	14–16	37	39–42	65	86–89
10	14–16	38	39–42	66	86–89
11	21–23	39	43–47	67	86–89
12	21–23	40	43–47	68	86–89
13	21–23	41	43–47	69	86–89
14	21–23	42	43–47	70	86–89
15	21–23	43	58–59	71	86–89
16	21–23	44	59–61	72	86–89
17	28–32	45	59–61	73	86–89
18	28–32	46	59–61	74	86–89
19	28–32	47	61–65	75	27–28
20	28–32	48	61–65	76	39–42
21	28–32	49	61–65	77	24–26
22	28–32	50	61–65	78	59–61
23	28–32	51	61–65	79	39–42
24	28–32	52	61–65	80	86–89
25	28–32	53	61–65	81	61–65
26	28–32	54	61–65	82	86–89
27	37–39	55	61–65	83	70–71
28	37–39	56	61–65	84	90–92

Answers

1. thousand
2. million   thousand
3. million   thousand   hundred
4. billion   million   thousand
5. 906
6. 420,300
7. 2,305,000
8. 18,056,900
9. 560
10. 13,000
11. 689
12. 9,978
13. 978,597
14. 899
15. 458
16. 98,657
17. 226
18. 1,203
19. 29,370
20. 12,103
21. 65,164
22. 368,336
23. 1,519
24. 3,379
25. 19,193 tons
26. 71
27. 632
28. 21,114
29. 4,181
30. 46
31. 3,629
32. 58,234
33. 729,578
34. 2,764
35. 9,678
36. 152
37. 5,766
38. 11,114
39. 427
40. $15
41. 1,686
42. 1,323
43. 92,099
44. 672,282
45. 564
46. 4,680
47. 3,591
48. 51,120
49. 30,492
50. 249,390
51. 7,353
52. 25,774
53. 16,351
54. 2,510,316
55. 25,000
56. 28,000
57. $304
58. 46
59. 704
60. 286
61. 24r4
62. 613r4
63. 8
64. 41
65. 43r10
66. 80r17
67. 27r5
68. 62
69. 34
70. 45
71. 39
72. 24
73. 53 people
74. $26
75. 2,758 miles
76. 423 tons
77. $129
78. $5,940

Place Value in Whole Numbers
Practice 1
pages 6–8

1. 86	13	99			
2. 800	204	871			
3. 1,998	5,690				
4. 7	0	9	6	2	1
5. 8	3	2	0	9	8
6. 4	2	2	5	3	7
7. 9	6	7	1	8	

8. hundreds   400
9. tens   10
10. ones   6
11. ten thousands   70,000
12. thousands   9,000
13. hundreds   300
14. thousands   5,000
15. hundreds   200
16. ten thousands   70,000

Reading Whole Numbers
Practice 2
pages 9–11
1. *b.* six thousand, seven hundred
2. *a.* fourteen thousand, ninety
3. *d.* two hundred eight thousand
4. thousand
5. thousand
6. million   thousand
7. hundred
8. million   thousand   hundred
9. thousand   hundred
10. thousand
11. thousand   hundred
12. million   thousand
13. three thousand, four hundred ninety
14. eighty-two thousand, six hundred fifty
15. three million, nine thousand, twenty-five

Writing Whole Numbers
Practice 3
pages 11–13
1. *d.* 7,300
2. *c.* 325,000
3. *a.* 1,680,900
4. *c.* 1,495,000
5. *b.* 92,960,000
6. 507
7. 265,000
8. 18,400
9. 30,870
10. 4,008,200
11. 620,304
12. 80,065
13. 40,920
14. 1,280,000
15. 2,090
16. 60,500

Rounding Whole Numbers
Practice 4
pages 14–16

1. 30	280	5,020	700	1,470
2. 600	26,500	8,100	5,000	385,100
3. 19,000	7,000	414,000	10,000	66,000
4. 20,000	10,000	410,000	160,000	70,000
5. 100,000	3,600,000	40,300,000	200,000	9,000,000
6. 2,000,000	13,000,000	5,000,000	10,000,000	32,000,000

7. $2,870   8. $2,900   9. $3,000

10. 2,820,000   11. 2,800,000   12. 3,000,000

Beginning Whole Numbers Review
pages 17–18

1. 6
2. 5
3. hundreds
4. thousand   hundred
5. million   thousand   hundred
6. 7,080   7. 203,015   8. 3,027,400
9. 14,970   10. 15,000   11. 15,000

Addition Facts
Practice 5
pages 19–20

1. 13	11	6	15	3	6	15	11	7	9
2. 10	13	7	13	12	9	7	12	9	3
3. 16	9	8	8	10	10	10	12	7	14
4. 9	15	4	2	13	8	5	6	8	11
5. 11	5	16	6	10	14	13	8	11	16
6. 4	14	7	6	5	6	2	15	10	5
7. 12	10	9	17	11	11	8	9	8	4
8. 5	10	10	12	9	3	1	12	7	18
9. 14	9	8	11	4	13	7	12	11	14
10. 7	8	13	5	10	12	14	10	8	16

Addition of Larger Numbers
Practice 6
pages 21–23

A.

1. 86	89	87	99	75	91	79
2. 76	83	87	78	97	69	97
3. 598	918	675	798	978	696	
4. 698	977	786	779	694	797	

5. 9,398	9,968	9,947	7,976	5,887
6. 79,739	77,979	66,849	66,798	86,959
7. 967,908	399,996	898,897	976,947	

B.

8. 598	388	558
9. 767	977	699
10. 3,569	5,875	4,956
11. 6,478	8,546	9,679

12. 689 seats
13. 779 employees
14. 1,988 students
15. 77 trees
16. 1,875 square feet

Addition with Carrying
Practice 7
pages 24–26

1. 110	113	153	132	133	70	110
2. 131	141	124	111	142	42	170
3. 135	183	100	115	62	150	104
4. 170	122	141	55	104	130	123
5. 820	422	522	720	860	455	
6. 321	701	930	804	670	752	
7. 1,221	734	1,321	1,101	1,166	1,040	
8. 1,212	1,280	852	911	1,131	1,105	
9. 11,002	4,525	12,592	11,481	11,535		
10. 12,684	11,935	5,484	8,704	11,203		
11. 1,508,907	1,676,091	1,448,835	1,301,096			
12. 5,296	3,543	3,650				
13. 2,201	5,381	4,391				
14. 93,323	78,542	50,858				
15. 34,095	36,613	48,105				

16. 279 miles   17. 6,015 CDs   18. 55,188
19. 2,410,556

Adding Money
Practice 8
pages 27–28

1. $18.98	$3.60	$24.15
2. $.95	$23.98	$5.89
3. $257.40	$1.88	$31.00
4. $552.36	5. $25.68	6. $84.99
7. $94.95		

Addition with More Than Two Numbers
Practice 9
pages 28–32

1. 180	200	127	160	193	150	124
2. 2,264	1,597	1,825	1,610	1,139	1,724	
3. 1,614	1,670	1,766	791	1,822	1,249	
4. 2,908	1,832	2,472	2,420	2,280	2,691	
5. 118,661	123,554	70,030	54,577	103,734		
6. 118,899	227,962	216,221	165,040	161,308		
7. 3,263	2,263	2,031	2,513	4,047	2,179	
8. 811	1,276	1,005	1,696	969	1,648	
9. 2,130,082	2,220,384	1,689,670	2,083,538			
10. 2,797,167	2,065,485	1,267,625	1,560,030			
11. 5,734	9,182					
12. 9,451	2,918					
13. 915	849					
14. 7,065	1,282					
15. 10,002	4,714					
16. 9,886	2,072					
17. 76,113	93,862					
18. 57,885	22,788					

19. 465 calories

20. 494 pounds

21. $174.15

22. 3,799 students

23. $679.08

24. 68,464 votes

25. $203.43

26. 587 employees

27. $4.57

28. $153.35

29. $551.21

30. 13,591,688

Addition Review
pages 33–34

1. 689

2. 4,787

3. 899,569

4. 885

5. 888

6. 83,687

7. 153

8. 1,333

9. 12,180

10. 13,040

11. 6,962

12. 27,979

13. $33.75

14. $13.83

15. 9,115

16. 12,767

17. 267 miles

18. 40,840 people

19. $66.81

20. 2,695 people

Subtraction Facts
Practice 10
pages 35–36

1. 9	1	3	4	5	9	5	1	0
2. 7	2	8	7	0	4	5	8	9
3. 1	8	2	2	1	4	7	0	1
4. 7	7	8	6	3	8	4	8	0
5. 6	4	0	3	3	1	6	3	6

6.	3	9	9	8	5	5	0	8	3
7.	6	6	0	3	9	6	9	8	5
8.	9	2	4	2	7	3	7	9	5
9.	7	2	4	1	5	7	5	2	0
10.	4	2	4	1	0	6	6	2	8

Subtraction of Larger Numbers
Practice 11
pages 37–39

1.	51	21	30	50	32	41	3
2.	413	501	222	340	616	921	
3.	514	132	203	204	213	261	
4.	3,102	9,114	6,112	7,104	8,202		
5.	3,304	1,312	2,601	1,106	3,402		
6.	50,052	13,023	11,511	31,220	11,032		
7.	627	815	640				
8.	181	121	304				
9.	1,110	7,204	6,102				
10.	1,021	1,432	1,235				

11. 31 pairs of pants
12. 151 people
13. 192 years

Regrouping
Practice 12
pages 39–42

A.

1.	73	43	58	48	88	69	29
2.	67	74	29	67	19	87	39
3.	5	9	58	5	74	17	19
4.	14	16	56	25	18	19	46

B.

5.	889	589	179	688	178	269
6.	385	89	98	396	187	172
7.	72	172	142	92	141	81
8.	4,588	1,779	699	3,889	4,788	
9.	39,804	45,598	40,061	16,821	59,217	
10.	771,868	189,389	593,188	689,549		
11.	288,876	218,578	384,747	187,889		
12.	2,754	3,908	1,018			
13.	4,914	1,376	6,238			
14.	1,015	1,979	2,896			
15.	2,544	1,265	687			

16.	85,877	39,228	60,784
17.	54,189	62,628	46,779
18.	44,407	60,463	28,986
19.	64,219	68,626	26,749

20. 263 miles   21. 569 people   22. $26

23. $147.93   24. $6,576

Regrouping with Zeros
Practice 13
pages 43–47

A.

1.	464	849	229	609	717	189
2.	249	519	439	665	229	818
3.	209	149	638	828	477	359
4.	49	89	239	159	447	288

B.

5.	754	673	107	434	541	319
6.	767	41	185	223	214	462
7.	4,484	6,046	2,784	2,777	2,145	
8.	6,662	144	4,031	1,742	1,111	
9.	3,259	2,486	1,879	795	3,448	
10.	5,648	8,519	3,704	7,663	1,548	
11.	766	1,403	7,055	4,634	4,993	
12.	48,213	43,601	36,451	65,122	21,180	
13.	40,771	16,515	29,042	12,278	13,006	
14.	2,184	5,083	2,595			
15.	2,421	7,684	2,700			
16.	8,534	6,630	2,741			
17.	27,104	36,728	63,931			
18.	47,095	84,291	31,057			

C.

19. $3.21   20. 5,826 feet   21. $100,725

22. $383.15   23. $38,907   24. $4,375

25. 3,087 people   26. 1,894,000 farms   27. 8,788 feet

Subtracting Money
Practice 14
pages 48–49

1.	$7.11	$5.44	$.17
2.	$4.24	$1.61	$.83
3.	$11.79	$1.52	$17.21
4.	$6.08	$4.26	$.62

5. $13.01   6. $24.49   7. $15.64   8. $5.02

Mixed Operations
Practice 15
pages 49–51

1. $4.95 $10.00
      .85   –   7.45
    + 1.65 $2.55
    $7.45

2. $28.30 $380.00
     31.99   – 74.92
    + 14.63 $305.08
    $74.92

3.   187   1,500
      174   – 1,006
    + 645   494 pounds
    1,006

4. 192   420
    + 123   – 315
    315   105 miles

5. $49,520 $150,000
    + 61,395   – 110,915
    110,915 $ 39,085

6. $399
    – 75
    $324
    – 15
    $309

7.   535   2,500
    + 970   – 1,505
    1,505   995 calories

8. 126,387   427,342
     93,568   – 288,546
    + 68,591   138,796 people
    288,546

9. $605.00 $1,930.40
     549.78   – 1,698.86
      97.53 $ 231.54
    + 446.55
    $1,698.86

10. $806,000,000   410 + 195 + 80 + 65 + 53 = 806

11.
$$\begin{array}{r} \$80,000,000 \\ +\ \underline{68,000,000} \\ \$148,000,000 \end{array}$$
$$\begin{array}{r} \$195,000,000 \\ -\ \underline{148,000,000} \\ \mathbf{\$\ 47,000,000} \end{array}$$

12.
$$\begin{array}{r} \$195,000,000 \\ 80,000,000 \\ 68,000,000 \\ +\ \underline{53,000,000} \\ \$396,000,000 \end{array}$$
$$\begin{array}{r} \$410,000,000 \\ -\ \underline{396,000,000} \\ \mathbf{\$\ 14,000,000} \end{array}$$

13.
$$\begin{array}{r} \$195,000,000 \\ +\ \underline{80,000,000} \\ \mathbf{\$275,000,000} \end{array}$$

14.
$$\begin{array}{r} \$80,000,000 \\ 68,000,000 \\ +\ \underline{53,000,000} \\ \$201,000,000 \end{array}$$
$$\begin{array}{r} \$201,000,000 \\ -\ \underline{195,000,000} \\ \mathbf{\$\ 6,000,000} \end{array}$$

Subtraction Review
pages 52–53

1. 63		2. 512		3. 26,106
4. 3,510		5. 167		6. 4,699
7. 23,058		8. 130,797		9. 483
10. 1,085		11. 14,859		12. 219,065
13. 447		14. 5,555		15. 6,948
16. 4,264		17. $127.36		18. 18,352 people
19. $6.35		20. 7,558 pounds		

Multiplication Facts
Practice 16
pages 54–56

1. 18	42	16	33	80	7	55	32
2. 9	110	64	20	15	60	9	18
3. 0	35	36	88	24	84	27	14
4. 108	4	36	120	0	28	36	55
5. 16	24	21	72	70	4	44	96
6. 16	110	60	48	96	10	22	30
7. 54	21	2	12	77	48	6	0
8. 8	48	72	81	0	88	63	10
9. 2	50	66	27	5	8	12	20
10. 12	56	45	100	63	35	66	18
11. 40	44	42	48	50	12	80	25
12. 30	45	121	32	0	40	36	99
13. 0	144	36	56	108	90	15	60
14. 12	10	72	6	1	70	0	99

15.	40	72	24	0	54	33	84	24
16.	6	132	10	24	48	30	40	20
17.	22	49	120	14	30	0	77	3
18.	4	18	0	60	28	90	132	20

Multiplication of Larger Numbers
Practice 17
pages 58–59

1.	248	219	729	630	306	168	128
2.	159	640	148	126	637	300	568
3.	5,608	1,296	1,028	2,488	733	1,260	
4.	6,377	1,242	2,139	1,684	608	2,484	
5.	32,084	21,906	8,662	6,220	27,369		

Multiplication by Two- and Three-Digit Numbers
Practice 18
pages 59–61

A.

1.	4,544	1,302	1,826	648	3,128	5,307	693
2.	7,917	1,449	2,350	2,232	4,536	1,376	1,008
3.	7,488	16,566	16,082	7,248	4,290	13,216	

B.

4.	29,280	172,451	146,286	163,013	59,099	68,688
5.	399,091	198,448	69,173	178,083	33,855	169,092
6.	2,689,363	1,569,984	2,222,020	2,529,052	2,326,569	
7.	452,658	1,371,824	4,796,350	1,594,880	285,483	
8.	3,137,968	1,383,269	708,080	1,145,716	511,839	

Multiplication with Carrying
Practice 19
pages 61–65

A.

1.	228	84	228	441	252	384	270
2.	174	585	156	477	272	588	114
3.	376	385	38	438	396	672	224
4.	135	656	318	273	352	648	105
5.	552	511	356	608	476		
6.	235	204	504	372	594		
7.	2,028	438	3,123	2,784	4,270	3,892	
8.	5,663	6,354	3,256	2,012	1,045	3,648	
9.	4,060	6,880	2,040	3,600	1,710	2,680	
10.	14,481	22,944	38,801	55,488	22,344		
11.	3,128	374	928	4,810	2,808	5,415	2,352

12. 19,180	35,712	7,452	14,857	42,552	22,204
13. 45,214	21,018	23,760	12,516	13,160	36,114
14. 13,376	31,992	18,404	22,575	44,408	53,508

B.

15. 4,920	920	1,110	5,180	580
16. 3,010	3,880	3,900	1,380	1,900
17. 2,580	3,160	1,100	4,400	3,220
18. 706,500	485,012	113,680	213,150	479,184
19. 34,612	18,387	26,100		
20. 36,894	16,296	78,690		
21. 123,240	218,892	660,816		

22. 1,026 tickets   23. $490   24. $216
25. 1,066 words   26. 84 feet   27. 720 cans
28. 288 ounces   29. $3,168   30. $4,300

Multiplication by 10, 100, and 1,000
Practice 20
pages 66–67

1. 820	270	680	590
2. 5,280	6,360	7,980	4,320
3. 9,290	5,410	2,360	5,720
4. 3,600	4,500	7,200	9,900
5. 3,900	7,600	5,200	4,700
6. 63,400	78,700	51,200	65,600
7. 23,000	47,000	90,600	40,500
8. 2,000	3,000	9,000	7,000
9. 8,000	17,000	26,000	5,000
10. 30,000	50,000	40,000	20,000
11. 387,000	634,000	911,000	286,000

12. 5,300 pounds   13. 40 quarts   14. 528,000 feet
15. $25,000   16. $897,600   17. $1,950

Estimation
Practice 21
pages 68–69

1. 45,000 feet   2. 53,000 feet   3. 47,520 feet
4. $2,400   5. $2,000   6. $2,556
7. 180,000 feet   8. 200,000 feet   9. 192,960 feet

Using Formulas
Practice 22
pages 70–71

A.

  1. 1,716 miles   *2.* 310 miles   *3.* 267 miles

  4. 444 miles   *5.* 20 miles

B.

  6. $26.95   *7.* $104.93   *8.* $14.04

  9. $28.00 $13.44 $14.85 $56.29

Mixed Operations
Practice 23
pages 72–74

  1. $267 \times 40 = 10,680$

      $10,680 \times 12 =$ **$128,160**

  2. $9 \times 12 \times 6 \times 4 =$ **2,592 people**

  3. $15 \times 27 = 405$ 405

      $12 \times 33 = 396$ + 396

                      801 pounds

  4.   283

       365

    + 344

      992    $992 \times \$5 =$ **$4,960**

  5. $56 \times \$37 = \$2,072$ $2,500

                      − 2,072

                      $ **428**

  6.   5,000,000   30,000,000   110,000,000   180,000,000

     10,000,000   50,000,000   140,000,000   220,000,000

  7.   50,000,000

     − 5,000,000

     45,000,000

  8. 1880   10,000,000

          ×   5

         50,000,000

9.
$$
\begin{array}{r}
220{,}000{,}000 \\
-\ 50{,}000{,}000 \\
\hline
\mathbf{170{,}000{,}000}
\end{array}
$$

10. $\$9{,}900 \times 220{,}000{,}000 = \mathbf{\$2{,}178{,}000{,}000{,}000}$

11.
190	160	110
90	50	40

12.
$$
\begin{array}{r}
190 \\
160 \\
+\ 110 \\
\hline
\mathbf{460}\ \textbf{full-time workers}
\end{array}
$$

13.
$$
\begin{array}{r}
90 \\
50 \\
+\ 40 \\
\hline
\mathbf{180}\ \textbf{part-time workers}
\end{array}
$$

14. $460 \times 40 \times \$15 = \mathbf{\$276{,}000}$

15. $180 \times 30 \times \$13 = \mathbf{\$70{,}200}$

Multiplication Review
pages 75–76

1. 1,248	2. 2,788	3. 21,361
4. 1,806,969	5. 665	6. 7,254
7. 4,704	8. 19,620	9. 48,981
10. 195,638	11. 4,312	12. 14,094
13. 27,504	14. 589,095	15. 49,000
16. 1,285,000	17. 400 passengers	18. 1,200 tapes
19. 1,344 cans	20. $462	21. $4,680
22. 2,790 words	23. 100 miles	24. $8.61

Division Facts
Practice 24
pages 77–78

1. 7	4	9	8	8	1	7
2. 4	7	4	9	6	6	8
3. 4	1	6	2	9	8	3
4. 9	1	5	1	6	4	2
5. 8	1	6	6	1	8	7
6. 7	6	7	3	4	8	2
7. 5	5	2	5	5	2	8
8. 9	6	3	7	9	9	1
9. 3	2	9	2	5	4	3
10. 4	6	3	9	5	2	7
11. 3	5	4	7	3	2	8

Division by One Digit
Practice 25
pages 78–82

A.

1. 48	76	93	64	72
2. 86	47	73	45	56
3. 98	27	76	83	59
4. 62	94	57	68	72
5. 312	846	327	652	
6. 931	478	529	637	
7. 263	479	386	752	
8. 384	866	582	678	
9. 5,673	8,872	2,456	3,287	
10. 5,014	7,608	9,032	2,409	
11. 8,046	9,067	3,307	4,301	
12. 9,153	3,385	3,678	7,832	

B.

13. 390	704	830	507
14. 804	960	470	580
15. 337	954	468	247

16. 8 yards   *17.* $1,250   *18.* 18 inches
19. $8,740   *20.* $2,642   *21.* $234
22. $840

Division with Remainders
Practice 26
pages 83–85

1. 47r2	86r2	38r7	49r3	75r1
2. 89r6	72r1	98r4	27r3	39r5
3. 26r3	48r5	92r5	73r3	69r1
4. 70r2	50r4	70r2	80r5	60r6
5. 67r4	94r2	57r5	47r2	89r1
6. 414r3	726r5	268r4	381r5	
7. 972r1	874r3	364r2	921r3	
8. 607r2	580r5	940r6	563r6	
9. 590r3	408r2	320r6	704r3	
10. 363r1	912r3	749r1	628r3	

11. 5 shelves   *12.* 1 foot   *13.* 13 coffee tables   *14.* 3 feet

Division by Larger Numbers
Practice 27
pages 86–89

1. 9	5	7	3
2. 4r20	7r30	5r15	6r12
3. 82	73	45	62
4. 56	24	71	64
5. 52r7	37r14	43r16	78r4
6. 52r20	41r40	26r15	62r13
7. 70	60	80r22	40r30
8. 488	546	247	368
9. 913	838	753	662
10. 702	308	460	740
11. 368r22	669r26	916r30	352r14
12. 21	76	93	34
13. 86r200	35r300	54r100	71r50
14. 60r80	30r60	70r100	90r200
15. 3	9	6	8
16. 6r22	5r12	7r14	4r21
17. 81	47	63	
18. 390r20	480r11	504r12	
19. 6	8	7	
20. 45	71	52	
21. 86	92	67	

22. 43 bags   *23.* $543   *24.* 36 cases
25. 12 gallons   *26.* $72   *27.* 4 miles
28. 47 weeks   *29.* 7 hours

Using Formulas
Practice 28
pages 90–92

A.
 1. $R = 144 \div 3 = $ **48 mph**
 2. $R = 276 \div 4 = $ **69 mph**
 3. $R = 102 \div 6 = $ **17 mph**

B.
 4. $T = 344 \div 86 = $ **4 hours**
 5. $T = 1,265 \div 55 = $ **23 hours**

C.
 6. $(77 + 95) \div 2 = 172 \div 2 = $ **86**
 7. $(\$124.60 + \$88.90) \div 2 = \$213.50 \div 2 = $ **$106.75**
 8. $(892 + 1,116) \div 2 = 2,008 \div 2 = $ **1,004 pounds**

D.

9. $(20 + 14 + 17) \div 3 = 51 \div 3 = \mathbf{17°}$
10. $(\$29,600 + \$17,080 + \$5,250) \div 3 = \$51,930 \div 3 = \mathbf{\$17,310}$
11. $(784 + 615 + 215) \div 3 = 1,614 \div 3 = \mathbf{538}$ **miles**

E.

12. $\$132 \div 12 = \mathbf{\$11}$
13. $\$192 \div 32 = \mathbf{\$6}$
14. $\$108 \div 36 = \mathbf{\$3}$
15. $\$1,200 \div 25 = \mathbf{\$48}$

Mixed Operations
Practice 29
pages 93–96

1. $216 + 108 = 324$
   $324 \div 9 = \mathbf{36}$ **square yards**
2. $\$24 \times 36 = \$864$
   $\$864 + \$150 = \mathbf{\$1014}$
3. $\$16,000 + \$14,500 = \$30,500$
   $\$52,000 - \$30,500 = \$21,500$
   $\$21,500 \div 2 = \$10,750$
   Jeff gets $\$16,000 + \$10,750 = \mathbf{\$26,750}$
4. Manny gets $\$14,500 + \$10,750 = \mathbf{\$25,250}$
5. $\$498 - \$122 = \$376$
   $\$376 \div 4 = \mathbf{\$94}$
6. $\$290 + \$15 + \$30 = \$335$
   $\$335 \div 5 = \mathbf{\$67}$
7. $\$175.00 - \$67 = \mathbf{\$108}$
8. $\$108 \times 5 = \mathbf{\$540}$
9. $\$540 \div 30 = \mathbf{\$18}$
10. $119 \times \$2 = \mathbf{\$238}$
11. $40 \times \$3 = \mathbf{\$120}$
12. $34 \times \$6 = \mathbf{\$204}$
13. $7,854,000,000 \div 119 = \mathbf{66,000,000}$ **acres**
14. $2,740,000,000 \div 40 = \mathbf{68,500,000}$ **acres**
15. $1,921,000,000 \div 34 = \mathbf{56,500,000}$ **acres**
16. Company A 5,000   Company B 2,500   Company C 1,500   Company D 500
17. 2 times
18. 500 cars
19. 75 cars
20. 7 pictures
21. $\$20,250 \div 15 = \mathbf{\$1,350}$
22. $\$295 \times 15 = \mathbf{\$4,425}$
23. $\$4,425 + \$20,250 = \mathbf{\$24,675}$
24. $\$24,675 \div 3 = \mathbf{\$8,225}$

Division Review
pages 97–98
1. 56
2. 297
3. 804
4. 32r4
5. 65r6
6. 709r2
7. 8
8. 43
9. 53r10
10. 37r15
11. 70r12
12. 72
13. 26
14. 63
15. 18
16. 84
17. $5,400 ÷ 12 = $450 monthly rent
18. 1,872 ÷ 36 = 52 yards
19. 864 ÷ 48 = 18 hours
20. $2,944 ÷ $128 = 23 months

Final Review
pages 99–103
1. million   thousand
2. million   thousand   hundred
3. billion   million   thousand
4. million   thousand
5. 2,040
6. 18,900
7. 3,006,800
8. 14,270,000
9. 700
10. 20,000
11. 588
12. 7,789
13. 496,794
14. 598
15. 397
16. 89,494
17. 205
18. 798
19. 59,143
20. 13,343
21. 209,685
22. 144,196
23. 2,259
24. 4,268
25. 3,935
26. 22,971
27. 51
28. 241
29. 14,144
30. 6,613
31. 46
32. 2,547
33. 28,907
34. 139,676
35. 348
36. 87
37. 1,267
38. 19,769
39. 207
40. 3,454
41. 16,506
42. 6,464
43. 1,648
44. 1,696
45. 175,908
46. 993,762
47. 783
48. 2,820
49. 4,704
50. 26,320
51. 13,662
52. 270,816
53. 6,482
54. 34,203
55. 11,328
56. 1,002,915
57. 28,000
58. 470,000
59. 82
60. 307
61. 463
62. 32r4
63. 81r5
64. 432r3
65. 9
66. 36
67. 28r30
68. 60r12
69. 40r30
70. 56
71. 38
72. 48r18
73. 58
74. 61
75. $120
76. 97
77. 224 miles
78. 378 miles
79. $2,457
80. 68 pounds
81. 1,296 bottles
82. 9,346 pounds
83. $21
84. 12 hours